The Seven Principles
of RESPECTisms

The Seven Principles of RESPECTisms

The word on the streets

KEN BARNES

NEW EYES PRESS

The Seven Principles of RESPECTisms

Copyright © 2007 by Ken Barnes

Published by New Eyes Press
The Bridge
12-16 Clerkenwell Road
London
EC1M 5PQ

W: www.respectisms.com
E: thehopedealer@respectisms.com

ISBN 978-0-9557489-0-5

Logo Design by Trevor Zimmerman from Tinsel Media

The 7 Principles of RESPECTisms

An average story tells. A good story guides.
This story illustrates, demonstrates and inspires.

Contents

"One Hundred Years from now... it will not matter what type of car I drove, or what house I lived in, but that the world may be a better place because I made a difference in the life of a child." *Forest E. Witcraft*

Foreword

What's our favourite day out I ask? A day at the fun fair may be the reply for many a young man or young girl. A day to ride the roller coaster of life full of fun and adventure, when you can push your meeting with fear to its limit within the knowledge that all will be well.   Life is very much a roller coaster and for an increasing number of young people in our society, the speed of change seems to be much harder to cope with.

How many times have we heard that young people have lost the ability to be respectful in their daily lives? Have we bred a generation of people who care only for themselves, cocooned in a world of make belief and removed from reality?

The values of honesty, trust and respect having been central in the development of our society across the centuries are in decay, ebbing away on a tide, gaining strength with ever depressing media coverage of daily events.

Against this fast flowing current are individuals who are devoting their lives in trying to stem the flow. Ken Barnes is one of those individuals.

Working alongside young people in the heart of the inner cities he has devoted his life in helping them regain values that have become blurred in our society.

Not only does he want those individuals to regain their own sense of identity and values, but to lead the 'crew' in providing a base on which to build future generations we can be proud of.

In 'The Seven Principles of RESPECTisms' Ken is able to capture the true feelings of young people in our society, and using their own experiences he begins to build the values we need in showing true respect.

'The Seven Principles of RESPECTisms' provides us with an opportunity to explore what drives young peoples' lives.

Each experience in the book provides young people with an understanding of how they can make a difference in their life.

Read on and join Ken in trying to stem the flow.

John Ratcliffe, Headteacher

Aknowledgements

$\mathfrak{T}$ogether we can achieve that which no one can achieve alone. There is one fact about success I am sure of, that is that nobody has ever achieved success entirely on their own.

The creation of this book has been an example of great team effort. I would like to extend my sincere thanks to everyone that has assisted me in the development of this book.

From the listening ears that must have got tired of me repeating the stories over and over again, to the helping hands that work so hard with me to get the look and feel of the book right.

I thank you all, I could not have done without you.

Introduction

Gandhi once said "We must be the change in the world we wish to see." I had always considered myself a conscious person, aware and concerned about raising the aspirations of young people - but what was I doing about it?

The question I eventually asked myself was not just whether I was concerned, but whether I was concerned… enough.

I came to the conclusion that if I was concerned enough that my talking had to go beyond the Sunday dinner table, and I had to roll my sleeves up and get involved in the process of affecting change.

When my first daughter was born, it reinforced to me why I had to be involved in the process of change.

If I wanted the society my daughter was to grow up in to be a better place, then I had to be involved in not only asking the questions, but also in finding and implementing the answers.

In my heart, I knew back then that my participation was going to be about changing attitudes, changing habits and in turn, changing the lives of the people I came into contact with.

Napoleon Hill once said, "What the mind of a man can conceive and believe the man can achieve." In my mind I could see myself making a difference to young people.

I also truly believed that I could make a difference. So with a heart full of passion and a determined mind, I entered the business of motivating minds, inspiring action, awakening dreams... and changing lives.

I became a supplier, a dealer, and young people were my customers/clients. I was not a dealer of pessimism or dope, but a dealer in a brighter future full of hope. *'The Hope Dealer'* became my name, and inspiration was my game.

The fact that you have picked up this book to read shows that you want change or to gain some further improvement in your life. Greatness in your life is yours for the taking...just believe that you can have it.

This book can help you on your journey to achieve it.

The principles in this book will provide you with a source of strength and inspiration that will prove invaluable as you set out to make your mark on the world.

Principles that as one person once said will give you a 'cheat code', giving you the answers to some of your future life challenges before they happen to you.

I believe that many of the youths of today are becoming an increasingly isolated population, faced at times to make decisions about their behaviour and adulthood based on media images and their interactions with their peers.

This book is about the character building life skills you need to make responsible decisions in your life. Life skills are just as important as academic skills in preparing you for your future life.

Life skills are those skills or characteristics that create the building blocks that enable you to reach your full potential.

How often do we hear that young people today don't respect themselves or anyone else? Newspapers and television are full of examples of disrespectful behaviour, which seem to suggest that not much can be done about the problem.

The fact is, many of today's youths are respectful of themselves, their parents and teachers, but these children do not gain the attention of the media.

Developing respect is an active process, and it begins with believing that respect is a right, not a privilege.

Respect yourself, respect others and always act in a manner that earns the respect of others.

Give respect and get respect. Respect for self and others are so important to me that I have used the word 'respect' to deliver some of the most powerful and life sessions to the young people I work with on a daily basis.

I found they had trouble at times remembering the success principles they had learnt from my sessions, so I developed a powerful and effective way for young people to retain the life changing principles they had learnt while also allowing them to embed the principles into their mind.

I took the word respect and turned it into an acronym that contained seven principles for successful living, which are so easy to remember. I call them collectively *'RESPECTisms'*.

'RESPECTisms' can be defined as the collective character building traits of the word respect when it is turned into an acronym, which outlines the principles of *'Responsibility, Education, Say No, Peers, Expectations, Consequences and Time'*.

As you read this book, you will discover more about the seven principles and how I have used the lives of seven characters to reinforce their principles and your learning.

As you read about the characters you may find one of them you can relate to, or you can relate it to someone you know. That's great, because that's just what this book is intended to do, to stimulate thought.

One word of advice - when you have read this book share the principles with anyone you can, especially your friends. That way your learning will be reinforced and multiplied many times.

Sit back, relax, read and enjoy as you discover the seven principles of RESPECTisms that have inspired thousands of young people over the years.

You will laugh with them, cry with them, cheer with them and learn with them, as they describe how the principles of RESPECTisms have affected and guided them through their lives.

Who are the seven young people?

How did they meet?

What happens to them?

Well, I shall keep you no longer. I shall let the story unfold.

This book is about impacting your life in a way that motivates you to strive to be the best you can be.

Sit back and enjoy as thousands of young people have enjoyed over the years *'The Seven Principles of RESPECTisms'*.

RESPECT isms

How It All Began

If you were to ask me how we all ended up together, I could not tell you… it just happened. Originally, it was just Sarah, Tracey and me (my name is Robert). We had known each other for a while and had always hung out. You know, the type of friends that do just everything together.

If one of us got into trouble, you could bet your life that the other two were involved in some way.

I must say though that about a year into secondary school, we each started to change and develop more of our own unique characters and traits.

Tracey began to take her school work more seriously at times.

Sarah must have had a really severe talking to by her mum, as she started to say "No" to me when I asked her to do some of the fun things we used to do that often got us into trouble.

Yes, I know, you have guessed it by now, I was the one who

always got the three of us into trouble, never taking life seriously and not taking responsibility for my actions.

Even though everyone else was changing, we still kept in contact and had some good times together.

The Meeting In The Park

It was the beginning of the six week holiday and all three of us decided to go for a fun day in our local park. There was going to be live music, stalls and a fun fair and the weather was great around that time, so we all decided to go.

I remember the day well. I was really angry because Tracey, as usual, was never on time and turned up late. Sarah was also late since she could not say no to some other friend because she had done him a favour.

We arrived at the park in the middle of all the action. The music was pumping and the atmosphere just seemed so full of energy and fun.

As we walked through the park on our way to the front of the stage, we saw a lonely figure sitting on a park bench that we recognised as a school friend of ours named Peter.

This was unusual for Peter as he had always seemed the kind of guy who liked to be in big groups, never wanting to be by himself. The last group he had joined did not look that friendly, and we wondered whether he had left them or had they kicked him out?

Sarah asked him if he was okay and he snapped back with a question, "Don't I look it?" Sarah immediately backed off and with this Peter stood up and apologised for his rude manner, and said that he had found out some things about the group he was jamming with and decided that he did not like them anymore.

His voice was croaking and he looked so lonely that I said, "Look, if you want you can stay with us for the day." There was no hesitation. Peter straightened his back smiled and said "OK, what are we all going to do then?" We headed straight for the front stage.

...And Then There Were Four

As we were walking, Peter's phone rang. It was his cousin Emma asking him what was up, and whether she could spend some time with him.

Before we could stop him, he had invited her down to the park to join us. "Great!" we thought, not only had Peter joined our group for the day, but now we also had to spend time with his cousin Emma, who we had heard was very spoilt and expected things to always be done her way.

That day Emma must have had a jet bike because it seemed like as soon as Peter got off the phone then she was there in all her glory.

So then there were five of us. As Emma was ranting on about what she wanted and expected from the day, I tried to shut off and turn my attention to whatever else was happening around me.

As I glanced across the park, there in front of my eyes was another school friend of ours, Colin. He was about to take a mobile phone out of someone's jacket on the back of a chair.

Not sure what came over me, but I shouted out, "No! Colin, what are you doing?" He looked across at me startled and embarrassed that he had been seen and proceeded to put his hands back in his own pockets.

He tried to put on an innocent grin and said, "Whatever you think, I was not trying to take the phone. I don't care what you saw, it was not like that."

I knew differently, and even though I did some irresponsible things, I would never have stolen anything. So I called him over, asked him what he thought he was doing and told him the consequences of his actions if he had been caught.

He looked so ashamed at that point that I felt sorry for him. So, I said that he could also join the group for the day if he wanted. At least that way, I thought, we could keep him out of trouble, and we could keep an eye on him.

The six of us pushed our way to the front of the stage to see who the next act was. To our surprise, it was another guy we all knew called Eddie.

He was known as the 'the school nerd' and was in the year above us. It was a poetry reading competition and we all had to agree that Eddie did very well. He was really creative and brainy like that.

When he came off the stage, he ran straight over to us, and we congratulated him. He had back stage passes, so we asked him to join us for the day.

That way we could all go back stage and meet the artists.

Little did I realise, that moment was to be the start of a great friendship of seven young people from different backgrounds with very different personalities.

The Seven of Us

We could never have known how much we were going to bond, grow, learn and develop into young men and women together. What we were about to learn about each other was that even though we were all different, the one thing we had in common was respect for each other.

Even Colin, with his tendency to do things without thinking or caring about the consequences at times... once he was with the group he acted differently.

It was as if we all fed off each other and valued the friendship enough not to do anything that would upset the apple cart.

The only person that would sometimes upset the harmony of the group was Emma, with her spoilt self. But to her credit, she would always come back round quickly and apologise for her selfish behaviour when she expected things to go her way and they did not.

The Crew

Once we realised that we were all going to be spending lots of time together, Peter with his group mentality suggested that we give ourselves a name.

There were loads of groups around at that time and most of them seemed to have the word 'crew' in it, so we thought since we could not decide what name we wanted, we would just call ourselves plain old 'The Crew'.

Around a week after first naming ourselves, the brain box of the group, Eddie, realised that if he took the first letters of our names (Sarah, Robert, Eddie, Emma, Peter, Colin and Tracey) and rearranged them, then it would spell the word 'RESPECT'.

Since we wanted our group to stand for something positive, not like so many of the other groups that were around, we unanimously agreed to add the word 'respect' to our original name 'The Crew'

So, that's how we became known as 'The RESPECT Crew'.

When I look back it amazes me how young people from different backgrounds and cultures with different personalities and personal issues can come together to form such a strong bond and friendship.

It has taught me that one of the main things in a friendship is respecting each other and valuing and appreciating each other's differences.

And boy, were we all different in our own ways, especially when it came to our personalities, which came out in each of us in very different ways.

Our Issues

We all either had a serious problem or were over anxious about certain aspects of our lives. You can guess what my main problem was? Yeah got it in one, I was not a 'responsible' person since responsibility to me was the other person's role.

Sarah just did not know how to 'say no' to people. So, she would get asked to do things that would either put pressure on her or get her into trouble. And yet, she just could not say "no". She simply did not like to let people down.

Tracey used to really annoy everyone with her time keeping since she was never on time. You know how it is, she was the type of friend that promises and promises that she will be on time. But, each time you end up waiting for her to arrive late with yet another excuse.

Eddie was a nerd. For example, some people when you see them they always have a smile with them. With Eddie, however, it was a book. He was so wrapped up in his 'education' that his childhood took second place and even he had to admit that he was boring and dull. And if he did not admit it, Emma was always on hand to tell him enough times.

Now Emma, she was so spoilt that things had to be her way or no way. She always had an 'expectation' that things should be done in a certain way... especially her way and when they weren't, she would have a fit.

Funny, the only person she would not really try it with was Colin. Maybe this was because he just did not care about most things, he did not think about the 'consequences' and she knew he just would not have it. And, if she started on him then she would have gotten as good, or even better than she could give.

Not forgetting Peter, who just could not stand to be by himself, he always had to be in a group. In fact, he seemed really afraid of being alone.

Downside was at times he was a sucker for the peer influence of a group and it sometimes got him into situations that were not, shall we say, the best for him.

So that was us… yeah, we all had our issues, but also in some strange way we also had a message to give to the other members of the crew.

Looking back, we did not realise at the time that we were learning from each other including even the bad points.

It was as if each of the RESPECT Crew members' lives either served as an example or a warning to the other members.

Do you have some friends whose lives can help you to either learn what you should be doing or what you should not be doing?

I think we all have, and the RESPECT Crew was no different since you could have made a story out of each one of us to serve as a positive or negative message.

The Story Begins

Looking back I know what mine would be. It was a story of a young man who did not take responsibility seriously and how it affected his life.

Would it be a positive or a negative story? Well, that depends on how you view it. I tell you what… you make up your own mind, as I have decided to tell you my story and then you can make your own opinion.

I am going to ask the other members of the RESPECT Crew to tell you their stories also.

I have never told a story before… I wonder how I should begin? I know. Settle down, as you are about to discover more about seven young people with seven different issues and how these issues, these 'isims' and 'schisms', became known as RESPECTisms.

This is our story.

The First Principle

Because of the nail, the shoe was lost. Because of the shoe, the horse was lost. Because of the horse, the rider was lost. Because of the rider, the battle was lost. Because of the battle, the kingdom was lost. And all was lost because of the horseshoe nail.

RESPONSIBILITY

My name is Robert, this is my story.

I **was the type of child where responsibility**, was the other person's job. It was never... is never, and could have never been my responsibility to do anything that I did not want to do.

'It's not my responsibility', was usually the thought in my mind. It was the perfect get-out clause for every bad situation I got myself into. In fact, "it's not my fault," or "it's your job, not mine," were my favourite sayings.

Not taking responsibility for my actions even justified me doing some really stupid things, and made it easy for me to not grow up or be serious about anything I did not want to be serious about.

The amount of times I would argue with my parents, teachers and anyone else who tried to tell me off regarding something I had done, or even what I should or should not be doing.

I always managed in my mind at least, to justify why I had or had not done it, even though the people around me were less than convinced.

In my mind it was so and that was all that mattered to me.

My dad, in his efforts to make me think about my actions more would always repeat one of his many sayings to me, "When the student is ready, the teacher will appear."

> 𝔚𝔥𝔢𝔫 𝔱𝔥𝔢 𝔰𝔱𝔲𝔡𝔢𝔫𝔱 𝔦𝔰 𝔯𝔢𝔞𝔡𝔶, 𝔱𝔥𝔢 𝔱𝔢𝔞𝔠𝔥𝔢𝔯 𝔴𝔦𝔩𝔩 𝔞𝔭𝔭𝔢𝔞𝔯.

I think he meant, when I was ready to grow up and start acting responsibly I would one day see the error of my ways and start to change my irresponsible mindset for the better.

I could never have known how right he was. What's more, I could never have known how my lack of responsibility for such a small thing in my mind could have caused such a horrible set of events to take place.

The Teacher Appears

The day 'the teacher would appear' started like any other for me. I woke up late for school, so I had to get up and rush and get my things together. In my rush, I turned my room upside down looking for my course work, which I had not finished yet, but wanted my teacher to go over some things with me.

I grabbed my bag and set off for school. As I left, I heard my mum shout out to me about picking my younger sister up from school. I pretended not to hear her as I thought, it's not my job to pick her up. Anyway, I had other plans.

I got into school just in time and ran to my first class, which I was late for because I had stopped in the corridor to speak to someone as if I had nowhere important to go.

We recently had a test and the teacher was about to hand out the results when Steve, one of my classmates, started his usual round of classroom antics.

Classroom Antics

Did I have to get involved? If you had asked me back then I would have said "yes." I would have said that he made me and I had no choice, but to retaliate. However, the truth was that I enjoyed it, and I did not have to.

On noticing us messing around the teacher shouted "Behave yourself, Robert and Steve!" Our usual response was, "We are not doing anything, miss!" We then got into our usual exchange of "yes, you were" from our teacher and "no, we weren't" from myself and Steve.

I really wanted to pass this test, if the truth be known, but I had not taken it as seriously as I should of because of my constant messing around in class.

When the test results arrived I turned over the paper really slowly to reveal my score. To my surprise I saw an 'A' and quickly thought I had done great, I continued to turn the paper. That was when I realised that the 'A' was the beginning of the word 'Another' and after that word was the letter 'D'. "Another D" was written in big letters over my exam paper.

I was so upset, mad and annoyed by the thought of my teacher mocking me by putting 'Another D'. I was also angry with Steve for constantly putting me off in class and stopping my learning. I am sure there was someone else I blamed, however, the one person I did not blame was myself. It just could not have been my fault.

That was a long day in school and I left mad and still upset about my exam results. I went straight round to my friend's house, purposely forgetting that my mum had asked me to pick up my little sister from school. *How responsible was that?*

After a number of texts from my mum reminding me that I was her big brother and that I should always look out for her, I reluctantly went to pick up my little sister.

We got on really well and I loved her dearly, but she was just so annoying at times. I suppose that's how little sisters are.

The Phone Call

As I reached the school gate my mobile rang. It was Steve from school talking about the test results in school today. He was over the moon because he had gotten a good mark in the test.

I was so mad that the person who I considered was disrupting me in class got a far better mark than me.

I started to tell him what I thought of him and blamed him for my bad score. It soon turned into a kind of argument, which was still in full flow as I picked up my little sister and signed her out of school.

She was glad to see me, but I just was not interested in her, I was in full flow with Steve, trying to get my point across.
Annie, my little sister, had stepped on her shoe laces and they had become undone.

When she saw me she asked me to tie them for her. I just said "Tie them yourself, Annie, you're a big girl now." I was so engrossed in my conversation that I could not be bothered with her.

As we left through the school gate, I shouted "Come on, Annie!" But, I was so deep into my heated argument that I did'nt realise that I was walking off ahead of her. I continued walking and did not bother to look back to see where Annie was.

Eventually, I had walked so far ahead, that I had crossed the road without her.

The Teacher Was Here

Something made me stop, turn and look back. As I turned round I saw her about to start crossing the road after me. I thought, "shit!" as to my horror I saw a car coming down the road really fast.

I shouted to Annie "Stay there!" in a vain attempt to get her to stay still and wait for me to come back.

She had one foot in the road. I could see that she was not going to listen to me as the car was getting nearer. I started to run back to her shouting "No! Annie, no!" and as I did, she started crossing the road towards me.

"No!" I shouted again, "No!"

It was too late because she was in the middle of the road with the car fast approaching. I stretched out my hands in a vain attempt to grab her even though I was ten feet away.

"Run! Annie, run!" I shouted as I now realised that she was in the road and the only thing was for her to run across quickly. She looked up at me and started to run across the road.

My heart started to beat, and even though it was a cold day, I instantly started to feel hot. It was as if the world had slowed down and I was watching everything in slow motion.

I can still hear the sound of the car brakes to this day as the driver of the car slammed on his brakes as he tried to avoid hitting her.

"She is going to be hit," I thought, "she is goona to die... oh no!"

Some people are reminded of their childhood irresponsible antics by memories of being told off, a failed exam or even at times, a criminal record. My lasting memory of what I considered to be my irresponsible nature was the sight of my little sister in a wheelchair.

You see, the car had just missed my sister. Thankfully the driver was very experienced and swerved just in time and chose to run into a parked car rather than my sister.

However, because I had not taken care of her and had not been responsible and tied her shoe laces when she asked me to, she tripped over her laces just as she got to the other side of the road after the car had missed her.

Her fall was horrible to watch. It all happened in slow motion as she fell forward and banged her head on the pavement so hard that it knocked her unconscious.

I remember looking at her as she lay there on the ground, looking so lifeless. I remember shouting "Annie, get up... Annie, get up!" But, she did not move.

I began to scream "Help! Help!" and the driver of the car ran over. He leant over and felt her pulse and said "She's not dead." He called an ambulance and stayed with us until it arrived. I remember sitting in the ambulance thinking "It's all my fault."

If I had only tied her shoelaces when she had asked, not taken the phone call, not ignored her, not walked so fast, been more responsible, cared more, then she would not be here in this ambulance, fighting for her life.

Mum and Dad told me at the hospital that the doctors who examined her said she had a blood clot on the brain, which was caused by the fall. They were not even sure if she was going to be all right.

After a number of tests and time in hospital they said she would be okay. But, they did not know how much of a recovery she would make.

I remember laying on my bed, praying and crying nearly every night for God to make her better. Thankfully, after three months she started to show some improvement, but she could not walk so I had to push her around in a wheelchair.

She was a strong girl and after a year she began to walk a little again. She eventually got better, but each day was a reminder of how my irresponsibility made my little sister unwell. How the small act of me not tying her shoelaces led to a tragic event.

The student was ready, but why did the teacher have to give me such a painful lesson by using my sister as the lesson content. During her time in hospital, I made a promise to myself to grow up and be more responsible.

In a strange way, the horrible events of my sister's accident had a positive effect on me. I began to reflect on the true meaning of responsibility, and I began to take much more responsibility for my actions and for my future.

The Turn Around

Through that lesson, I learnt that to become responsible is really about becoming response-able. It was about my chosen response to things, and that it was up to me to grow and develop my ability to accept and respond positively to the things that happen in my life.

That being responsible was part of growing up and becoming a young man. I also learnt that it should not have taken a tragic accident for me to see the error of my ways, for sometimes learning that way may be too late.

One of the first things I decided to respond better to was my education. I accepted that it was within my control, and I could choose to shut out any distractions and focus on my school work.

I called on the one person I knew well enough that I felt could help me in my education, 'Eddie the Nerd'. He was great. He helped and supported me so much over the next few years, and I have him and my teachers to thank. They changed so much in the way they engaged with me when they saw I was really trying to succeed in school.

Eddie was a brilliant educational mentor and a friend, he loved education and education seemed to love him. However, Eddie had his own issues, some which were so deep rooted that they came out in his behaviour and aspirations.

This is Eddie's story.

The Second Principle

Education is the key to success; it gives you choices.
You must learn day by day, month by month, year by
year in order to broaden your horizons. Education is the
most powerful weapon you can use to change the world.
If you study to remember, you will forget. But, if you
study to understand, you will remember.

EDUCATION

My name is Eddie, this is my story.

The **first memory I have of my parents**, in fact, the first memory I have of my life was of my parents arguing in front of me.

They were so wrapped up in themselves that they forgot that their five year-old little boy was a ringside spectator who was about to be emotionally scarred by what he saw and heard.

It was not a physical fight as such, but tempers were flaring as my mum told my dad that he was no good and that he should go out and get a job and support his family.

His reply was that "he tried," but no one was prepared to give a job to someone who could not read and write properly, and that because he had a hand injury he could not even get a job as a labourer because of the lifting involved.

"You're no good!" Mum bellowed at him. "You should have stuck at school instead of playing truant and messing around… you're stupid, stupid, stupid!"

The Hope Dealer - Education gives you greater choices in life.

23

My Dad's Regret

My Dad looked so angry and frustrated. He hated when mum reminded him that he could not really read or write. He really regretted his childhood actions of messing around in school. It was just the way for a number of his friends back then and he followed.

I never forgot the three words my mum had said… "You're stupid, stupid, stupid!" and had no idea how those words were going to affect my future. It was about three years later that we went to my aunt's house for dinner. She could really cook, so I was always willing to go.

The Graduate

She had a twenty-two year-old daughter that she was so proud of because she was very clever. The topic over dinner was her forthcoming graduation. She had obtained a first in her degree in business studies and was about to graduate.

My parents were invited, but dad said no. I suppose he did not want to be reminded of his lack of education, as education would be the talk on everyone's lips at the ceremony. I said to my mum, "Can I go please?" I just wanted to see how my cousin looked in her gown.

The day came around so quickly. We arrived nice and early, yet the venue was full of proud parents and excited young people waiting for their turn to be called up to graduate. They all looked so great in their outfits and my cousin looked fantastic. You could have seen her proud smile from a mile away.

The Graduation

At the end of the ceremony they had a guest speaker. I cannot remember his name, but everyone liked his speech, especially me. There was one part of it that stuck in my mind. He said, "Education is the key,

Education gives you more choices in life. Education can lift you out of poverty into a life of abundance."

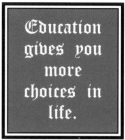

I asked my mum what the word abundance meant. When she told me, I knew one thing for sure; our family was not living in abundance. In fact, it was more like poverty.

I remember once when my mum and dad had an argument because my mum had eaten the last slices of bread, and we did not have any money to buy another loaf until Wednesday when my dad got his dole cheque, which was two days later.

Mum did not have any money as she was pregnant at that time with my little sister and could not work. We were poor. We lived in one room with a curtain, which was drawn across the room at night to give my parents some privacy.

My bed was a sofa bed, which I rolled out every night. I had no idea where my sister was going to sleep when she was born.

My alarm clock some mornings was a loud SNAP, which was the sound one of the five mouse traps in our room made when one of its unsuspecting victims got its head crushed in a vain attempt to get the cheese secured on it.

If I ever got a hole in any of my clothes I would get a beating as they would ask where they were supposed to get money to buy me some new ones. New ones! That was a joke as my parents were the junk and second hand clothes shop's best customers.

The shop had a fancy name like 'Born Again Wear'. The clothes, in my mind, should have stayed dead as most of them looked as if children had lived in them about thirty years ago.

Education Gives You Choices

'Education is the key. Education gives you more choices in life. Education can lift you out of poverty into a life of abundance' went through my mind as I reflected on the speech I had just heard.

It was at that moment, I decided that education was going to set me free. Education was my route out of a life that I hated. Education would stop me being like my father, and I vowed to learn as much as I could.

My Awakening

At the age of eight, I was inspired to make a commitment to my education and from that moment on, my books became my best friend. In fact, they were my only friends as I consumed myself with reading and learning.

It was not long before I began to shine in my class and get compliments from my teacher. I loved it. I could not wait to rush home and tell my mum that I got another 'A', or a positive comment from a teacher.

My dad in the meantime started to drown his feelings in booze and used to come home drunk singing, "My old man, said follow the van and don't dilly dally on the way… da da da...." I don't think he knew the song completely, or he was too drunk to remember the rest of the words.

He was not interested and did not even want to hear about my success in school. He knew he could not help me with my homework so he just stayed away from the subject altogether.

I began to be known as 'Eddie the Nerd'. At first this name caused me a lot of pain because I was teased every day. I even had my own place on the school wall where people would write horrible things about me.

I was different from most of the kids in my school. I was a loner and no one seemed to like me because I was always into my books, early for classes and seen as a teacher's pet.

I was never invited out to the parties, never invited around anyone's house to play and the girls never wanted to talk to me. I just was not, as they put it, cool and I would cramp their style.

As much as I felt disliked, in some strange way, I also felt very respected for my education in school even though they did not openly show it.

'Education, education, education', was my motto. Most of the time, I did not care about anything else as I truly believed that education was my way out of poverty and a life I hated, as I had been told some years ago by the speaker at the graduation.

I can only remember one period in my life when education was not at the forefront of my mind. In fact, at that time I did not care for education at all.

Girlfriends and Me

I was fifteen years-old, and just as any fifteen year-old would say, you somehow did not feel complete unless you had someone you could call your girlfriend.

From the outside looking in, most of the boys in my school were on their third girlfriend at least by the age of fifteen. I had the distinct honour of being the only boy in my class who had never had a girlfriend.

I had never even held a girl's hand; they just did not like me.

As a consequence of them not liking me, I decided that I did not like them. This mindset worked well for me until one sunny spring day when it happened. Just after half term, the size of our class rose from 30 to 31 when we had a new person join the school.

This was no ordinary, new school kid. In my eyes, she was beautiful. You could not have told me differently because she was smart and she loved her education. She also seemed to have something in common with me. She looked like a loner... 'a beautiful nerdess', I thought, what a team we would make.

The Wrong Strategy

So after planning for around two months, I made my move and asked her out. There was a new author launching his book at a café and I thought this would have been the perfect place to take an educated girl like Mavis.

Her response was as unexpected, unwelcome and as painful as a kick up the backside when you're not looking. In fact, it would have been better if she had done that. At least it would have been between me and her and no one else.

I made the naïve and fatal mistake of asking her out when she was within ear shot and sight of some of the other girls in school. Mavis, in her nerdess attempt to gain some street cred, used me as battering ram, and promptly answered my question at the top of her voice. She said, "Pardon, are you asking me out? I would never go out with someone like you, you're a nerd and you're boring. Don't you know girls just want to have fun? You don't look like fun in any way, you nerd! Get lost!"

The Pain

It was like a knife piercing my side in slow motion, and I stood there and took it. All I could hear was laughter coming from all sides of the room and the person laughing the most was Mavis.

That day was the first time I bunked off school. I just could not face the rest of the afternoon with all the sniggers and comments.

I cried myself to sleep that night. Once again I recalled the words of the speaker at the graduation. "Education gives you choices," he said. "But you forgot to tell me it was not a choice of girls!" I shouted out... as if to tell him to shut up.

The next morning I went to school scarred with the memories of the events of yesterday. I thought I would keep to myself more than normally.

We had an exam that day and as I looked at the paper I thought, 'nerd', 'boring', 'girls just want to have fun'. It seemed like the boys who were messing around in school got all the girls and had all the fun.

So, I did something that would have seemed unthinkable a week ago, I purposely flunked the exam paper. I thought for once I would have something in common with the other boys in my class and they might start liking me if I was not so smart anymore, and I started to play up in school.

After a couple of months of antics, which surprised every one of my teachers, I had the grand total of no more friends, no more people accepting me and a red letter home to my parents. That was the colour of a letter when there was a problem at school.

The Confrontation

I remember getting home that evening and my dad and mum were waiting for me. The shock of receiving the letter had awoken my dad's interest in my education.

First, my mum started by telling me how disappointed in me she was. Dad just listened. When my mum finally went upstairs to look after my baby sister, my dad started on me too.

"You have been messing around in school, and you have failed your latest test paper," he started to say. This was not a good period for me. I had been rejected by the girl of my dreams, failed an exam paper, messed around in school, made no new friends, got in trouble and had a letter sent home. Now, my dad who could not even read or write properly was telling me off for failing an exam paper.

You're Stupid, Stupid, Stupid!

I just exploded and shouted at my dad "You're the failure, you're the failure!" and repeated the words I had heard my mum use many years ago. "You're stupid, stupid, stupid! You're the one who can't even read or write properly."

My dad went what seemed red, then blue and raised himself out of the seat while screaming at me "Who do you think you are talking to, boy?" At just over six feet, my dad was not a small guy and the sight of him raving mad was enough to stop many men in their tracks.

I froze with terror. I actually felt like I was going to wet myself and waited for the beating that was about to come.

The Moment

Then, something happened. He just collapsed in a heap and fell back into the chair with his hands *(which I thought were going to be around my neck)*, cupped with his head buried in them.

There was a moment's silence. I then heard him say, "I am sorry, son. I should be the one saying sorry." He continued, "I am sorry, son, for being a failure, failing you, failing your mum and failing the family."

I had never heard my dad speak in this way before; he was a proud man despite his lack of education.

In an almost tearful voice he said, "I have not been all I could to myself, which has stopped me from being all I can to you and the family." My emotions were now quickly turning from what was anger, to fear, then sadness.

With tears in my eyes, I said, "Dad, you have not failed me or mum or baby Sue."

"I have," he continued still with his head in his hands. "I have not been able to provide for you properly because I am a failure. I was a failure at school, and I have been a failure in my life. Don't grow up like me, son."

I could not see his face to know for sure. It was only through the sight of the wet specks on the newspaper where he sat, that I knew that my dad was crying.

On noticing my dad in such an emotional state, a man who I had at times feared because of his size and mannerisms, I suddenly for the first time in our father/son relationship felt I had to now become the comforter.

I walked towards him. Each step I took pressed the tears from my eyes into the carpet, as I was now crying uncontrollably. I leant over him as he sat still in a heap in the chair and whispered into his ears what were to become life changing words for both of us.

As if by destiny, I had been reading a book on success principles earlier on that week. I repeated the words, which had touched me so much.

I said "Dad, I love you. You have cared for us to the best of your ability all my life. You are not a failure. You may have failed at some things as we all do in life, as I have just failed my exam. But, the only time you become a real failure is when you give up trying, and you have not given up on us, have you, dad? You have not stopped trying, have you, dad?"

There was a long second pause. My dad lifted his head to reveal his tear stained face and said, "Son, I love you and this family and I will never give up trying to do right by you all."

The Turning Point

Our silent embrace after those words seemed to last forever and ever. Who cared, I was in a place that I had never been before with my dad and I did not want it to end.

We did not realise it at the time, but the experience we had shared inspired both of us in different ways. My dad plucked up the courage after that day to go on an adult learning course on basic reading and writing and then went on to gain a diploma.

From that moment on, I stopped trying to be the 'fool who was cool' without education, and went back to my old self as the 'nerd who was going to be heard' by the world. I was gonna to use my education to make a difference to people's lives.

I began to see education as a gift that I could share with others as I had shared it with my dad. I began to see education as not just something that happens in school. It was something that happens every minute of the day, wherever I was.

An interesting lesson I was to learn later on in my life was that far from making you a nerd, as you got older, your education separated you from the crowd and made you confident and sexy.

Education and Choices

Where did the word 'sexy' come from? Well, it was the word that a girl I picked from my choice of girls had used at the launch of my first book of poetry entitled 'Ramblings of a Poetic Nerd'.

The speaker at my cousin's graduation some years ago was right. Education can set you free. Education can move you out of poverty. And yes, education certainly gives you choices of the nicest kind, as my dates with at least three of the girls from my book launch made me aware of.

Education was my way out of my childhood experiences. It was how I was not going to live like my parents had lived. It was about me having the freedom to choose.

Not everyone in 'The Crew' had freedom to choose how their education was going to affect their life, as the decisions that they had made beforehand made the choices for them.

Sarah made some choices in her school life, which led to circumstances that would limit the future path she could take.

This is Sarah's story.

The Third Principle

It is tough to be the only one who says 'no', but you can do it. Paying attention to your own feelings and beliefs about what is right and wrong can help you know the right thing to do.

SAY NO

My name is Sarah, this is my story.

𝕴 **felt so ashamed of my mum**. After my dad had left, she just had a string of boyfriends one after the other. Some of them used to last a while, but most of them were short-term.

They were all my uncles. Yeah right! That was until I was old enough to know the difference, and then my mum stopped caring what I thought and told me she had a life too, and she was going to live it.

She never showed me any real love. She said she cared for me, but I could not feel it. She said she loved me, but I could not feel it in her actions. I grew up as a child yearning for love and affection.

There was one so-called uncle who had a son who would have been my cousin, if my mum had been telling me the truth when she said he was my uncle from my Dad's side. He was down from Manchester with his son and needed somewhere to stay.

Joe and Me

His son's name was Joe and we got on very well. We lived in a block of high rise flats, and we would play out together all the time. For the first time in my life, I felt like I had a real brother. He was older than me so he used to look after me as well.

As usual, that relationship did not last long. I was so upset because Joe was the first male to show me that he really cared about me and now he was going.

Even though he was only one year older then me, he was the closest thing I had to a father like figure who looked after me.

I said my goodbyes and went back inside my house, tearful at the loss of someone I really cared about. Looking at my mum, I was angry.

I was also confused since my mum had always done everything she could for the men I saw her with. Whatever they asked her for, she had done it like she could not say no. But, they still either left or she sent them packing.

Anyway, I was sure I would see another 'so-called' uncle turn up soon and went to my bed and slept.

A Buff Boy

Soon after Joe left, another boy who I grew to care about came into my life. But this time it was different. He was not the son of an uncle or one of my mum's flings.

He was a boy in my school and he was so buff! *(That's good-looking if you did not know).* His name was Mark.

We grew very close, and I really liked him. I would have done anything for him. I again felt needed and wanted by someone. I was not being shown any attention or love at home, and he made me feel really special when I was with him.

Whatever he asked for I would try to get it for him. Even when he started asking me for money, it still did not occur to me that this boy may have had some bad intentions for me. That did not matter. I got the money when he asked even if I had to borrow it from someone. I just could not say no to him.

Sometimes, I would really want to kick myself for being so soft with him. Why was I always trying to please him? Why did I do whatever he asked?

Whenever I sat down to think about it, thoughts of my mother would always run through my mind. Could I in some strange way be acting the same way my mum had been acting all my life with my so-called uncles?

"No!" I thought. I do not want to be anything like my mother. She is a tart who does not have any respect for herself and let's men walk all over her. I could not be like her. The thought was scaring me, and I would dismiss it every time.

Another thing that scared me around that time was Mark's constant talk of sex. He knew my age and knew how I felt about it, but that did not stop him. He was in the year above and a number of his friends had lost their virginity already and I knew he felt left out.

Mark's House

His mum and dad loved the theatre and were going to see a play at the weekend. He said that he needed some help with his school work and asked if I could come round once his parents had gone out to help him. I thought nothing of this as I was quite good at school and felt needed by him when he asked for my help.

When I got to his house, the first thing I noticed was that there were no school books to be seen anywhere. When I asked him where his work was, he just said that we should watch a movie first, and then he would go and get his books to do some work.

I must admit, I did feel uncomfortable, but as usual, went with the flow of things. It was during the film that he started on me. We used to kiss a lot, but that was all. But this time, I could feel that he wanted more, a lot more.

As he kissed me, he said if I let him go all the way, then he would never leave me and that we would spend the rest of our lives together growing old.

My father had left me, a number of men in my mum's life who I had grown to like had left me, and even Joe had left me. So, the thought of him never leaving me was so good, it made me feel so safe.

The Act

If you asked me how it happened, I could not tell you because it happened so fast, very fast. All I remember is that one minute we were kissing, and he was on top of me. Then, it was all over and he sat on the other end of the chair with a smile as wide as a Cheshire cat.

We had done it, we had had sex without any protection. "Shit," I said in my mind. I should have said no, but I clearly did not. Now, I had had sex with a boy for the first time.

It was not what I imagined it would have been like, and even afterwards was not nice as less then ten minutes later he was rushing me out of his house telling me his parents would be back soon.

"What about your school work?" I asked. "Don't worry about that, we will do it another time," he said. With that, he rushed me out of his house.

I left his house feeling very low and knowing I had done something very wrong. But, I could never have imagined how the next chapter in my life was to unfold.

The next day, I walked into school and this strange feeling came over me that everyone in the school knew. Either he had told everyone or they could tell by the way I looked or was walking. I was so paranoid.

I did not see him all morning in school, but knew I would see him in the dinner hall since we always sat together in a group of about eight of us.

That day was to be different. He was in the hall, but he was with another group of boys for the first time in months. They were laughing and joking. I had no idea what they were talking about, but clearly knew he was ignoring me. I felt so hurt.

I had given in to this guy for a feeling of acceptance, but at that moment, all I felt was rejection, and it hurt like hell. I bunked off school the rest of the day because I was so upset.

Over the next few weeks, he did speak to me, but it was never the same. We never spent any time together alone and we never did anything together.

I used to cry myself to sleep most nights. I even thought it was my fault. What had I done to him or not done for him, I asked myself.

I Could Not Be

It was around four weeks after the event when I woke up one morning and suddenly thought "Oh my God! I have not had my period yet." I looked in my diary. I should have had it six days ago. I was never late.

I began to think of all the excuses I could that would explain why I was late. Stress, tiredness or even just one of those months. These excuses seemed good until I was three weeks late! No, I could not be pregnant! I thought, not after just one time, my first time... no! I was starting to get really concerned and decided that I had to know.

I remember how I took the bus and traveled about two miles away. I just did not want to buy the pregnancy test in a chemist near me, I just couldn't do it. I got back home and my mum was out, so I went to the bathroom and carried out the test.

It was one of the pregnancy test sticks that showed a line in the middle of the circle if you were pregnant. It took about five minutes before I could look at it. My eyes were closed and I opened one of them slowly and glanced at the pregnancy stick with one eye.

I could not see anything that clearly, so I just said in my mind "here goes," opened both eyes and held the stick up to see what it said.

In Mark's house, I had crossed the line by not saying no and having sex with him. What I now saw was another line exactly where I did not want to see it. One that said... I was pregnant.

I quickly put the pregnancy stick in my bag as I heard the front door opening. It was my mum coming home. I am not sure why, but for the next few days, I pretended that it had not happened, and that I was not pregnant.

The Confession

What made me face up to the fact that I was pregnant was my teacher talking with me a few days later about my options for the next year and me realising that my options were now limited. I burst into tears. My teacher put her arms around me, and I told her everything, from the incident in Mark's house, to me being pregnant.

My teacher told me the first thing I needed to do was tell my mum. The thought of that really scared me. Even though my mum had me when she was only sixteen, she had always told me that if I ever got pregnant, she would pack my bags and throw me out.

When I told my mum, she was so angry. "How could you be so stupid?" she asked. "I cannot believe you allowed this to happen, you silly girl." My mum did not throw me out, but she said she was grounding me for eight weeks. I'm not sure why since it had happened already!

Next, I thought, I need to tell Mark. I could not face him, so I called him, but I put the phone down when he answered. I thought I would send him a text and let him know what had happened, thinking he would then call me back.

I sent the text and waited for the call. I waited and waited, but the call never came. So I picked up the phone and called him. His mobile was off. I could not believe it, I felt so alone, so rejected and so angry with myself. If only I had said 'no' to Mark at his house, I thought, this would not be happening to me.

> "If only I had said no to Mark"

It was the start of half term and I did not see or hear from Mark for a week. He would not take my calls or return my calls or texts. On the first day back at school, I was determined to confront him and ask him why he was ignoring me.

I caught him in the corridor and told him to his face that I was pregnant and that the baby was his and asked him "What do you think we should do?"

The Rejection

His response was a complete shock to me. "Why you telling me for? If you are pregnant, it's not mine. Go and speak to the other guys you have had sex with, or get rid of it," and with that he stormed off with his friends.

Not only had he insulted me by suggesting that I had sex with other boys, he had said it so loud, that everyone in the corridor had heard.

Now the whole school would know I was pregnant. I just remember running and running until I was out of the school gates and not stopping until I got to one of my favourite spots, a bench under a tree in the park near school.

I had spent many a moment under this tree, thinking about all the wonderful things I was going to do with my life, and consider all the choices I had to make in terms of my education and career.

Now, it seemed the only choice that I had to make was whether I should keep this baby or not. Yeah, 'get rid of it' as Mark had said. I started to bang my stomach as if to destroy what I considered was about to destroy my life, but had to stop to wipe the tears from my eyes. "What shall I do?" I thought. And in that moment, I knew what I had to do and I got up and went home for the day.

The Decision

How would I do what I knew I had to do? What would people think of me? How would I cope with it? All these questions went through my mind.

I did not care, I just felt in my heart that what I was going to do was the right thing, even though when I spoke to a good friend of mine she disagreed and asked how could I? She said she could never do it.

It was a hard decision to make, but I had decided. I am not even sure why I was so certain that what I was about to do was the right thing. I just knew in my heart that I would regret it if I did any other thing.

I decided that no matter how much of an impact it would have on my life, I was going to have the baby.

The next few months were horrible. Apart from a few of my close friends, I felt so alone. It felt like every time I walked down the school corridor, walked in the street or went into a shop, everyone knew, and everyone was talking about me.

It felt as if I had a label on my forehead saying I had unprotected sex and now I was pregnant at fourteen years-old.

What made things worse was that Mark, to protect himself from being accused of not taking responsibility, started spreading rumours that I had sex with some other people he knew and that the baby was not his.

I now had the label of a school tart who was easy. Thoughts of how my mum lived flashed through my mind. Was I a tart? Did I deserve this? Am I becoming what I most hated about my mum?

A Horrible Experience

My pregnancy was a horrible experience for me. The morning sickness was terrible. I used to be just sitting there and I would get this feeling of sickness, run to the bathroom and then nothing would come.

When it did, it was as if my insides were coming out of me.

Then I had my mother constantly reminding me of how stupid I had been, and that I was lucky she did not throw me out. I had the shame of going to school with a big belly and having everyone look and stare at me.

They called me some horrible names, especially as Marks tactics had worked and I was now known as an easy target for sex. Some of the boys even tried it on with me, even though they knew I was pregnant.

I used to try and cover my bump with baggy clothes, but you could still tell I was pregnant by the fact that I put on so much weight in my face and developed big spots.

I was getting bigger and bigger and was being teased so much by the other students. There was a point I was so unwell, I could not attend school and I missed my end of term exams.

My education became messed up, so I decided to mess it up completely and I left school when I was five months pregnant.

Love vs. Rejection

In my search for love and affection, I had discovered in its place hurt and rejection, all because I did not say no. I was now a statistic, one who was pregnant at fourteen and missing out on her education.

If I could turn the clock back, what would I have done differently? Well I certainly would not have gone back to Mark's house, and I would have definitely had the strength to say no.

I consider that I did then and I do now have a right to say no, and that always saying "yes" to people is not a good way to get them to like you, as you leave yourself open to abuse. That if I said no, and the person respected me, they would understand.

During the next three to four months, I found an unlikely close friend. We just started talking one night for hours and hours, and even though we were friends before, the level we went to on that night sealed our friendship.

He began to always be there when I needed him or always got me something when I craved for it.

I would never have imagined me and Peter getting so close during that time, but we did. I think he could understand more than the rest of the group the pain I was going through when I was being rejected and how I felt alone at times.

What did we have in common? Throughout Peter's life, he had constantly battled with rejection and the fear and feeling of being alone to such an extent that it shaped his thoughts and actions.

This is Peter's story.

The Fourth Principle

It is not easy to resist the negative influences of your peers, but with inner strength and self-confidence you can stand firm, walk away, and resist doing something when you know better.

PEERS

My name is Peter, this is my story.

My mother was a doctor and my Dad was a dentist, so I came from a good home. I had a younger brother and an older sister and we lived in a six bedroom house.

Home was a lovely place, and we had everything we could need as children. Even though my mum and dad were both in demanding jobs, at least one of them was always there when we came home from school.

We had lots of love in the house, but we also had lots of rules. My dad used to be in the army and had developed a certain way he believed things should be done with no compromise, especially from his children.

Sometimes our home was so regimented, especially when it came to our chores and household responsibilities. They just had to be done at a certain time and in a certain order.

"Everyone has a responsibility to each other in the house," my dad used to say. He used to call our chores "character building". But to me, they were back breaking and his constant going on about routine was head hurting!

My Brother and Sister

My little brother, in my opinion, was spoilt. He was seen as so small and cute so he got away with many of the chores asked of him. Guess who had to do them? You guessed it in one. It was me.

I used to argue with my parents when they let my little brother get away with things. I just did not think it was fair. They would react by calling me spoilt and then have a go at me. I used to get angry and feel that my family did not understand me.

My older sister was really smart. She had left school and was in college aiming for her master's degree. Mum and dad were so proud of her.

So then there was the 'past cute and cuddly', 'not quite done anything to be proud of me'.

At times, I felt like the forgotten middle child.

There were many times when I had to play alone at home because my sister was out, which I was glad of, and my mum and dad were busy keeping my little brother occupied.

Why was I glad my sister was out? Well, this was because at times she was horrible to me. When she used to look after me if she got angry with me or anyone else, she would take it out on me and lock me in the broom cupboard for hours by myself.

I remember the feeling of being scared and lonely. One time, she even went out and left me still locked in the cupboard. To stop me from telling mum and dad she blackmailed me by threatening to tell my mum and dad about the day I got caught stealing bikes with my friends.

I had told my sister and the police that I was not involved, and I was not. But, it did not seem to matter because I was with the boys who did it, so they considered I must have been involved as well.

Mum and dad had no idea about this incident, and I wanted it to stay that way. So I never told my parents about how she used to treat me.

While in the broom cupboard, I would sit there making up imaginary friends that would come round my house to play with me.

Friends and Me

My dad never allowed me to bring any of my school friends home, and was always warning me of the danger of peer influence. He did not like the look of many of the children around where we lived.

I did not think they looked that bad, and I longed to have some friends near my home my age to play with and have fun.

There were some old garages near our home. I would always see a group of boys around there laughing, joking and just having fun. I was so curious about what they were up to that one day I decided to find out.

I climbed over the fence and headed down to the old garages. It felt a bit scary as it was getting a bit dark, but it did not stop me. As I approached the garages, I noticed that the boys were inside and all I could hear was laughter.

As I moved closer to the open garage door, I could hear what seemed like the sound of heavy breathing and paper rustling. I had always wondered why the boys always seemed so happy, but could never have imagined what I was about to find out.

As I peered through a small window at the side of the garage I saw them sitting with crisp bags in their hands. At first I thought they were just having a snack each, and I watched them as they lifted the crisp bags to their mouths.

However, they did not lean back to drain the last tiny bits of crushed crisps into their mouths, as we sometimes do when we come to the end of a bag of crisps. Instead, they were holding the bags over their mouths and quickly breathing in and out frantically.

I had no clue what they were doing! They were not eating crisps… so what could they be doing? It was then that I saw them reach into a bag on the floor and pull out a container.

They then proceeded to empty its contents into the crisp bags they held. Once again they lifted up the bags to their faces and started frantically breathing, as if to catch their breath.

They stopped for a while and seemed a bit dazed, and then, they all burst into a fit of uncontrollable laughter. They sat looking dazed for a while then started the whole process again.

After about half an hour of this, they got up to leave looking tired and pale. I did not want them to see me, so I quickly hid in the bushes behind the garage until they had gone.

I watched them leave and noticed that although they had shut the garage door, they had not locked it. They must be coming back soon, I thought. I was so curious about what I had seen that I felt I just had to find out more. So, I quickly entered the garage lock up.

There were a number of empty crisp bags littering the floor and the garage had a funny chemical smell about it. As I looked at the mess, I recognised the container they had taken out of their bag.

It was empty with no labels on it to say what it was, so I put it to my nose to see if it had a smell. It smelt like glue.

We had been given a drug awareness session at school the week earlier and solvent abuse had come up. So, I immediately understood what they had been doing. I turned around to leave, only to find one of them standing in front of me, and then, the other two appeared.

The Meeting

Instead of getting mad that I had found out their secret, they smiled and the tallest said, "I have seen you around the ends, what's your name?" I was so surprised since I expected to get a beating for coming into their space.

I replied in a nervous voice, "Peter."

He then said "Do you smoke?"

I had never touched a cigarette in my life, but because I did not want to seem like a wimp, I said "Yes, but not all the time." He handed me a half-smoked cigarette to share with him.

I was amazed. I had intruded into their space, caught them taking drugs, and they did not know me! Yet, they were being nice and wanted to share a cigarette with me.

Even though I did not smoke, I felt compelled to at least pretend. I took the cigarette, put it in my mouth and inhaled… at least it was not drugs, I thought.

The coughing must have lasted for at least three minutes as I tried to recover from the burning sensation in my lungs from inhaling the smoke.

The three of them laughed at me so much, and when I stopped coughing, I also started laughing. It was as if in that moment, we all bonded together.

My New Friends

After that day we met all the time in the garages. I could never let my parents know, as they would have gone bananas. "Don't ever knock on my door for me," I told them, "as my Dad will go mad."

Kevin, who seemed to be the leader of the group laughed, and then went on to tell me some of the issues he had at home. Then, David joined in and when he finished Tony said some things too.

I was amazed. I thought I was the only one going through what I was going through at home, and now I had found some kids who had something in common with me… their families did not understand them either.

We talked for hours, which bonded us together even more. I felt at that moment I had found some new friends, or so I thought. What I was to learn was that far from being my friends, they were actually "Frienemys".

I began to spend a lot of time with David, Tony and Kevin. I think most people in the area knew, except my parents, as I was always with them.

I was the newest member to the group, and I no idea of their past history. But, it occurred to me that it must have upset some people, as certain people in the area started acting differently towards me.

Show Me Your Friends

Firstly, it was the local sweet shop owner, who always used to speak to me. He had even left me in his shop once for five minutes while he went off to do something else.

𝕾𝖍𝖔𝖜 𝖒𝖊 𝖞𝖔𝖚𝖗 𝖋𝖗𝖎𝖊𝖓𝖉𝖘 𝖆𝖓𝖉 𝕵 𝖜𝖎𝖑𝖑 𝖙𝖊𝖑𝖑 𝖞𝖔𝖚 𝖜𝖍𝖔 𝖞𝖔𝖚 𝖆𝖗𝖊.

He suddenly stopped talking to me and whenever I was in his shop, he would follow me around with his eyes, as if I was going to steal something.

An incident that really upset me was when I was in the market and I overheard a group of people saying, "There goes that junkie boy who sniffs glue."

This really shocked me as I had never taken any illegal drugs in my life, and there I was being called a junkie by someone I did not even know.

Why were people thinking like this? I thought. Then, I remembered a saying my dad used to say to me, "Show me your friends, and I will tell you who you are."

The shopkeeper and everyone else had seen me hanging out with these boys and had come to their own conclusion.

I had been labeled. Just because I had been seen spending time with these boys, people's thoughts were 'junkie!' or 'petty criminal!'

I pretended I did not care because I liked my new friends, and they were good to me. I thought, if you do not like them, I do not like you.

I was about to get a reality check of just how good my friends were to me.

It's Not Safe

Around that time, there were so many boys and girls getting their mobile phones stolen. You could not use your phone in public through fear of someone approaching you to steal it.

A trick the thieves used was to ask you for the time. Then, when you took out your mobile phone to look, they would grab it from you and either run or get their friends to back them up so you could not argue with them.

The Frienemys Appear

It was a sunny day, one of those days when everything just seemed to be going right for me. I had a good morning at home, with my parents pleased that I had finished all my chores before I left the house.

I had a good day at school and was on my way home, thinking about dinner as I was starving.

I met Tony and Kevin on the bus heading home. We all sat at the top of the bus at the back. We always did that so we could see what was happening in the rest of the bus.

They were talking about how they were broke and needed some money to buy glue for their next sniffing session. They ask me if I had any money. I said I was so broke it was a joke.

As they began to think and discuss what they should do, a younger boy I knew from school came onto the bus.

As he clambered up to the top deck he had his mobile phone in his hand. He sat down and then realising who was on the bus, he quickly put the phone into his pocket.

About five minutes later, his phone began to ring loudly, and I could see he was hesitant about answering it. So, he let it ring for a while.

Tony looked at Kevin and Kevin looked at Tony, as if to say a secret code, which only they understood. The phone just kept on ringing. Then, the boy made the fatal error of taking it out of his pocket to answer the call.

I could hear from his replies that it was his mum asking when he was coming home. Not wanting anyone to hear, he whispered "…in half hour, mum… I love you."

Tony and Kevin got up from their seat and walked over to the boy. As the boy ended the call and lowered his hand to put the phone back into his pocket, Tony leaned forward, grabbed his hand and said "Give me your phone." The boy looked startled.

"No!" he said, and began to struggle. His refusal to give up his phone was met by a hard slap on the back of his head by Kevin, which resulted in the boy falling forward onto the metal rail in front of him and banging his forehead.

He still had hold of his phone when Tony opened his jacket to reveal a long kitchen knife he had been carrying. The boy quickly realised that his phone was not worth being stabbed over, and he released his grip.

Shocked at what was happening, I rushed to the front of the bus to speak to Tony and Kevin. I had never seen them act this way before.

As I approached them, a woman angered by what she was seeing, decided to stand up and confront Tony and Kevin.

By this time, I was right next to them and from our conversation you would have assumed I was with them, or I knew them at least. The woman started telling Tony and Kevin to give the boy his phone back or she would call the police.

Tony replied "Oh shut up, you old bag, call them then if you think you're bad." The woman reached into her handbag and took out her phone, placing her bag on the chair beside her and started to dial 999. By this time the boy who had just been robbed was in shock and just sat still with wide-eyes.

I was trying to reason with Tony and Kevin, shouting at them to just give the phone back and get off the bus and leave. They were having none of it. They were in their element, acting as if they were untouchable.

The Theft

As the woman placed the phone to her ear, Kevin grabbed her hand and knocked the phone to the floor. As she bent down to pick it up, Tony, seeing her bag open on the seat, helped himself to her purse.

The bus was getting so noisy with the woman screaming at the top of her voice and Tony and Kevin screaming back. Where did they come from so quickly? Who knows? Who called them? I do not know, but what I do know is that before I knew it, the police were on the top deck of the bus approaching us.

"What's going on here then?" one of the officers demanded.

"They took my phone," said the boy. "It was them three!" Them three, I thought! I was not involved! I only came over to stop them and now I was being labeled as a thief. My dad's going to kill me, I thought.

The officers must have had a long day because they said, "Look, if you hand the phone back, we will not take this any further."

Strange thing for them to say, but they said it. Tony looked at Kevin and then Kevin looked at me and then we all looked at each other. After what seemed liked a long pause, Tony took the phone out of his pocket and gave it back to the boy.

It was then we heard a woman's voice shout out, "My purse has gone! My purse has been stolen!" We all looked round to see the woman who had originally said she was going to call the police in distress because her purse had gone missing.

"They must have taken it" she said and pointed to the three of us. Again, I thought, I am being labeled a thief when I have done nothing, just because I am with the wrong crowd.

"Alright, you three stay here!" There was no light heartedness in his voice now because the police were not about to forget this crime even if her purse did turn up. The police officers emptied the top floor of the bus and then turned to us three.

"We can either do this here or at the station, which would you prefer? You have to be searched." Tony, whom I had seen take the phone, ran forward to be searched so quickly, I thought this was strange. The officer then proceeded to search Kevin and then I was searched.

The Set Up

"Is this your purse, madam?" I heard the police officer who had searched me ask. I was stunned, how did it get into my pocket? The policemen wasted no time in grabbing my arm and telling me, "Young man, I am arresting you in connection with ...." I started to think, "Oh my God! I am being arrested, how could this have happened?"

I turned to Tony and Kevin as I protested my innocence to the police officers. They had blank expressions on their faces as if to say, "What do you expect us to do?"

As the police officer led me off the top deck of the bus, I again wondered how this could be happening to me and the answer came to me.

In the commotion, just as the police officers came upstairs, Tony had been standing next to me. He must have slipped the purse into my jacket to avoid getting caught.

I was mad. I was angry! I have been stupid, and I felt such a big fool. These guys, whom I had called my friends, had just set me up for a crime and they seemed to be smirking. I had thought they were my friends, but really they were my 'Frienemys'.

'Frienemys' was a word I learnt from a mentor I had some time ago. A 'Frienemy' is someone who pretends to be your friend when they want something or they need to use you for something. I had just discovered the hard way how mixing with the wrong people can get you into trouble.

The officers led me away and put me in the back of the police car. I could see everyone looking at me and thinking all sorts of things. I was in the back of a police car and the handcuffs were hurting my hand.

"Can you take them off? They're hurting me," I asked the police officer. But, he just ignored me. I supposed he thought I was just like any of the other boys he arrested every day.

While I was in the police car, all I could think of was how my mum and dad were going to react to their son being arrested. We got to the police station quite quickly, and I was hustled out of the van into the station.

They led me straight through the back door into a cell. The sound of the cell door locking me in went straight through my body. I wasn't there for long when I heard the cell door being unlocked. The officer looked at me sternly and said "Come with me, boy!"

They are going to interview me now, I thought, do I need a solicitor? The police officer led me to the front desk.

The officer looked me in the eye and said, "You are lucky, boy. The woman and the boy from the bus have just been in and told us that it was not you who was involved in the stealing, and that it was your two friends."

Should I or Shouldn't I?

"Now, we are prepared to let you go, but you must tell us where we can find the other two boys." I was now faced with a dilemma. For me to go free I had to become a grass.

I thought for a moment, those boys did not care about me, so why should I care about them? This was not about being a grass though. This was about doing the right thing.

I told the officers what they needed to know and they let me go. It was a lucky escape for me since it could easily have turned out very differently.

"Do you want us to take you home?" the officer asked.

"No thanks, my parents would ask too many questions," I replied.

I should have read the signs earlier that Kevin and Tony were no good for me, but because I so desperately wanted to make friends, I ignored what was in my face, time and time again.

As I left the station and made my way home, I swore I would not make the same mistake again. I swore that I would make sure that I knew what my friends were about before I really started hanging around with them.

I thought about all the good things at home I would have missed had I been sent away for the crime of stealing the lady's purse. I was wrong. I had jammed with these guys because I thought they understood me, something I thought was missing at home.

What I came to realise as I considered my home life, was that it was not my family that did not understand me. It was that I did not understand my family.

My home was the way it was for a reason and my parents only ever wanted the best for me. I could not wait to get home to do my chores that evening.

What a lucky escape! Mixing with the wrong people could have landed me in serious trouble. It was a lesson learnt for me and one that I vowed never to repeat.

I decided that I was going to spend more time with my family and other relatives. I had an aunt who lived nearby. She did not have any sons, but she had a daughter who was around my age.

She was not really the type of girl I wanted to spend lots of time with as she was so spoilt, but I thought as she was family at least I could trust her.

As I got to know her better she opened up to me and told me of some of the things that had happened to her that made her act the way she did.

You decide if what happened to Emma would have affected you the same way.

This is Emma's story.

The Fifth Principle

I may have made mistakes but I am somebody. I may be young but I am somebody. I may not have always done the right thing, but respect me for one day I will be somebody.

EXPECTATIONS

My name is Emma, this is my story.

𝕴 **know what you're thinking about me already**. "Spoilt little kid who comes from a good home, has all the privileges and just wants to have things all her own way."

Well whatever you think, I don't care anyway because you really don't know me. Who are you to judge me? You don't know what my life has been like.

If you had been through what I have been through, done what I had to do... then, you would understand. But you have not, so don't you judge me.

Yeah, I may live in a nice house, in a nice area, have parents with lots of money, but it was not always that way for me. You see, the home I am in now is not my first home.

What I'm really trying to say is, where I live now is not really my parents' home because the people I live with are not my real parents.

The Way It Was

They adopted me when I eight years-old. My real parents and home were nothing like what I have now. My mother, bless her soul was a really humble woman.

Life had not given her much, and she had not expected much out of life in return. Even though she never went to church, she was, I believe, a very religious woman. Her favorite sayings were "The Lord shall provide" and "He that believes in the Lord shall not want".

Well, the Lord never really provided, and I believe my mother did not really and truly want, because behind all the prayers and the sayings she did not really expect anything more than what life had offered her already.

My Dad

My dad, on the other hand, had high expectations about many things. He always expected mum to dress a certain way. Like, she could not wear any skirt which showed her knees or any tops that were cut to low. He used to say "This is how I expect my wife to look."

He used to expect his dinner on the table when he came home at night from work.

He used to expect things done around the house in a certain order and way, and he used to expect his children to call him "Sir". Not "dad," but "Sir!"

He had worked as a plant manager in a local factory for fourteen years and had been expecting a major pay rise and promotion for the last four years.

Each year when his review came around and it did not come, he would come home mad as hell and take it out on us by being even more demanding.

What I could not understand was why he used to order so much stuff from the catalogue. How was he expecting to pay for it when he never got his pay rise or promotion? We just about got through on what he earned then and really could not afford any extra spending.

When my mum used to challenge him, he would snap back saying, "Don't worry, I know what I am doing, woman!" My mum would then ask him if he was sure and end by saying, "You're right, the Lord will provide."

In that home, the Lord did not provide for me. Whenever I wanted anything the answer always seemed to be "No!" I had very few toys. I used to have to use my imagination and play with household items when I got bored playing with the few toys I had.

The Incident

I was six when the incident happened. I still remember it like it was yesterday. We were around my dad's brother's house. They seemed to be the only family I knew except for an aunt on my mum's side.

It was a great atmosphere. I was having a great time all day and by the end of the evening I felt really tired. I asked my uncle if I could lie down. He told me I could go and lie down in their main bedroom.

I went upstairs and fell asleep. It must have been about thirty minutes later when I was awoken by the sound of the bedroom door opening. It was my uncle. He came in saying he was looking for something.

He started to talk to me, asking me how I was doing at school and how it was. I told him it was good and I was enjoying school. He stopped looking for whatever he was looking for and sat on the edge of the bed. For about two or three minutes he did not say a word. He just sat there staring at me.

When he did speak he said, "Come and sit on your uncle's knee."

This was an uncle whom I have played with many times, so I had no hesitation in sitting on his knee. As I did so, he put his hand on my knee and began to stroke my hair, running his hand all over my face.

As he did this, I could feel his other hand slowly moving up my left leg. He put his hand right up my skirt and began to try and take off my knickers. I tried to get off his knee, but he held me even tighter.

I attempted to scream, but he put his hand over my mouth. There was only one thing for me to do, I thought. I opened my jaw as wide as I could, and I clamped down my teeth and I bit hard into his hand.

The Words

I don't know where I got the strength from, but I bit his hand so hard he had to hold his breath for a moment. He grabbed me, threw me on the bed and then said some things to me I will never forget.

"You little cow... you ugly little cow!" No one had ever called me ugly before. It was the first time, and even though this man, my uncle, had tried to molest me, what hurt me most at that moment was that he called me ugly.

Angrily, he shouted, "Your mother has done nothing with her life, and your father is worthless, and you will also grow up to be nothing, just like your mum and dad."

His hand was bleeding. I could see the blood stains on the side of the bed he was on, which was matched by my tears on the side of the bed that I was on.

When my uncle saw the state I was in, he must have started to feel guilty as he said "Sorry, I am so sorry for what I have done!"

I was not listening. I ran straight downstairs into the arms of my mother, and I told her everything that had happened.

To my amazement she just said "Emma, we will talk about this when we get home." And, we said our goodbyes and left.

When we got home, mum and dad sent me to my room and after quietly speaking downstairs for a while, they came and spoke to me. The first thing they said was "Are you sure this is what happened, Emma?

Uncle Ted is a nice man and we cannot believe that he would do something like that."

I started to cry, "Yes mum, yes dad!" with tears streaming down my face.

"Stop that crying!" my dad said. "We have spoken to Uncle Ted and he says he cannot believe that you are saying these horrible things and wants to come and ask you why you are lying."

"No," I said. "I do not want to see him."

Unbelievably, Dad said sternly, "Look, I do not want to hear your lies, Emma. In fact, I do not want to hear you speak about this incident again, do you hear me?" I could hear by the tone of his voice he was very serious.

Afraid that I had done something wrong, I said tearfully, "Yes, daddy."

The truth was my parents did not want the shame that reporting my uncle to the police would bring on the family. So, they chose to just forget about it and just kept me away from him whenever he was around.

The After Affects

I don't believe they could ever have imagined how the incident was gonna affect me. I would have constant nightmares where I would be playing in my room alone and my uncle would come in. He would lock the door behind him and start walking towards me.

A sick feeling of panic would rise from my stomach, and I would throw back my head and let out a piercing scream. Then I would wake up in a cold sweat with hot tears streaming down my face.

I never ever told my parents about the nightmares. I did not think they cared so I kept them to myself. My parents, who were supposed to protect me, did the very thing I never expected them to do. They let me down, and what's more, they believed him rather than me, their daughter.

For a long time after, the anger, hurt and pain towards my mum and dad remained. I know I should have forgiven them, but the way they just brushed the incident under the carpet really scarred me.

Later, I was to discover that what scarred me even more than my uncle putting his filthy, dirty, smelly, nasty, hands on me, was him calling me 'ugly', and saying that I would never become anything.

For years after that incident I lived with a voice in my head saying, "You're ugly", "You're nothing and you will become nothing." I could not stop the voice in my head. It was there morning and night.

I am ashamed to admit that I hated my parents for a long time for not protecting me. Added to that, the fact that I was cursed by my uncle to be like them, meant that on that dreadful day, I did not cry.

The day of their funeral, I just stood with a blank expression on my face by their coffins as they were buried.

The Accident

How did they die? We had all been out to celebrate mum's birthday and on the way home, a drunk driver had gone through a red light and crashed into our car.

I remember seeing this bright light coming towards us, hearing my mum scream, and then hearing a loud bang. The car had hit us head on, killing my mum and dad instantly.

I was only saved because I was in the back seat with my seat belt on. I was the only one to survive, and I was now without a mother or father, an orphan and homeless.

My uncle, being next of kin, offered to take me in. I had no where else to go. I remember screaming and kicking as he and his wife tried to pull me in their car to go home after the police had informed them what had happened.

I ran away after one night and slept on the street, huddled in a shop doorway really cold and afraid. I was awoken by a police officer who took me down to the station. I told them everything. They went to my uncle's house to interview him, but of course, he denied it.

A woman from social services had some meeting with me and said if I did not want to go to my uncle's house, then the only other option was a foster home or adoption if I was lucky. That's how I ended up at the house where I am now.

My New Home

When I first arrived there, I was in a bad way with no parents, no love and no self esteem. I was ugly and I was going to be nothing. As my real parents had let me down so badly, I expected nothing from this new couple. I did not even speak to them for the first few weeks.

They were a nice couple who were just trying to help a little girl who had just lost her parents. They knew my history and had fostered a girl my age before who had been through even worse than I had been through.

They had felt they made some errors with her by pushing her too much, so with me they did the complete opposite.

If I did not want to do something, they just said, "OK, darling, that's your choice." When I did not want to go to school, they just wrote me a note.

They just wanted me to like them and they set no real goals or expectations for my life or education and would not push me either.

It was a complete turnaround for me from a home where I had practically nothing to a home where I had everything I wanted. From a home where I could not do anything to a home where I could do whatever I wanted.

I lapped it up and I began to develop a really bad attitude.

Looking back now, I do not even think it was my adopted parents' fault. I believe I was just angry with the world. I was an ugly girl in an ugly world, I thought, who would never achieve

> **An ugly girl in an ugly world.**

The Hope Dealer - Don't just meet expectations, exceed them.

69

anything. I was someone who had caused her uncle to molest her. Yeah, I was angry and I took it out on anyone I could by demanding that things be done my way.

The Pain

Underneath it all, I was just a little girl in pain. A girl who every time she walked past a mirror remembered her uncle's words "You're ugly." Every time I sat down to do anything that challenged me, like a test, I would remember my uncle's words "You're nothing and you will become nothing."

To top it all off, my adopted parents in their vain attempt for me to love them and not push them away, did not push me at all.

In truth, I was a girl with very low self-esteem. I had no real belief in myself and believed that my uncle's words would come true.

I know everyone thought I was spoilt, and yes, maybe in some ways I was. But, if the truth be known, the spoilt Emma was just a front for the Emma that believed she was nothing.

At least the spoilt Emma got listened to, at least the spoilt Emma was strong and confident, at least the spoilt Emma was somebody. This was unlike what I thought the real Emma was and could ever be. This was my way of covering up all the hurt and pain I had inside.

The spoilt Emma was the outer wall I had built to hide the real Emma. Little did I realise that the same wall I had built was also keeping the real Emma in and stopping her from coming out.

Inside I was a lonely girl who had no real friends, who felt ugly and with low expectations of herself. This was reflected in my school work and my very negative language at times.

It took someone, who I had teased for years by calling him all sorts of names, to bring me to a point where I could see that my behavior was destructive for myself and everyone around me.

The Party

A friend of ours had a party and everyone I knew was there. Anton was going to be there. He was a boy that all the girls in the school liked.

He was smart, good looking and always dressed well. Even though I felt the way I did about myself, I was determined to speak to him and try and get a date with him.

I saw him walk in and went straight over and began talking with him. We were getting on really well, I thought. As we were talking, Tamika walked in and I saw Anton's eyes move away from mine, looking straight at her as she walked by. For about thirty seconds, it was as if I did not exist.

Tamika was beautiful and she always had the boys chasing after her.

The Smile

As she passed him, she smiled as if to say hello and continued walking. Anton told me some feeble excuse and got up and followed her into the next room.

I was furious, I had him mesmerised until that bitch came swanning by with her smile and took the boy I was talking to away from me.

I went back over to my friends who had seen the whole thing.

"How could she do that?" they asked, "Why did she have to smile at him that way?" "She did it on purpose. Are you going to let her get away with that?" they all said at once.

I was mad, really mad. I wanted to find out what they were up to. As I walked back to the room, I passed a large wall mirror and stopped as I saw my reflection.

I had just seen a boy I was talking to choose a beautiful girl instead of me, so was I really surprised? No! All I could see staring back at me in the mirror was an ugly girl. One who would be nothing because she was nothing.

I paused for a moment, and then the spoilt Emma who always wanted things her way kicked in. I walked up to Anton and interrupted their conversation by asking, "Are we going to continue our conversation now?"

Tamika looked stunned and stared at me. I stared back and said, "Who do you think you are looking at? I was talking to him first." I started to raise my voice angrily, "Just because you're pretty you think you can have my man!"

"Your man?!" Anton said. "I am not your man, we were only talking, stop being stupid." And with that, he held Tamika's hand and walked off leaving me in the middle of the room by myself.

I wanted the ground to open up and swallow me. I had well and truly embarrassed myself because of my insecurities and spoilt manner. I felt a hand on my shoulder and heard the words, "Emma, its OK, let's go. Let's go for a walk and talk."

My Saviour

I remember Robert saying that he really believed in a saying his dad used to say, "When the student is ready, the teacher will appear." I suppose I was ready and the teacher appeared for me in the form of Eddie the Nerd.

At that moment, the guy who I saw as a nerd, whom I had teased and told off on many occasions was in front of me, willing to help me in my moment of need. We went outside. It was a warm night so we walked around the block.

I was feeling so sorry for myself and I wanted and expected pity from Eddie, but he gave me none. Instead he said, "I can see you feel sorry for yourself, but I don't feel sorry for you. This is all of your own doing". I raised my head up and looked at him in surprise at his frankness and honesty.

He continued "The only reward for self pity is more self pity and validation that you were right to feel sorry for yourself in the first place." Eddie was quoting some words he had learnt from the many books he had read.

I protested, "I don't feel sorry for myself. It's Tamika and Anton. They are so rude and thoughtless, like so many people I know!"

He stopped me in mid flow and said, "Emma, we don't see the world as it is. We see the world as we are, so if you always feel people are rude then maybe it's a reflection of how you feel inside."

Acting Ugly

"I feel good inside," I replied.

"Do you really?" said Eddie. "Then, why do you act so ugly?" he continued. He got the words 'acting ugly' from his little sister. She used to say it when people were horrible to her. At that moment I decided to step out from behind the wall I had built.

I told him, "I act ugly because I feel ugly." Then, I don't really know why, but I let it all out and told Eddie all about my life after he promised not to tell anyone.

Eddie was in the year above me and he was wiser than his age. After listening to my story he said, "Emma, of all the judgments you can pass in life, none is as important as the judgment you pass on yourself.

You have deemed yourself ugly, you have told yourself that you will be nothing, which is why you feel ugly and you feel like you will be nothing."

"No, its not me!" I cried, still resisting. "My dad and mum were nothing and they could not even stand up to my uncle who tried to abuse me… and also my uncle said I would be nothing… and it's true… it's all true."

The Hope Dealer - Don't just meet expectations, exceed them.

73

I was getting really emotional. "You nerd," I said. "You would not understand, you're going to be somebody, not like me, you're good at things not like me, you're... you're..." The tears came running down my face and interrupted my moment of self pity.

Eddie took his hand, lifted up my face, wiped away the tears from my cheek and said, "It is not what people call you that defines who you are, it's what you answer to that does."

He wiped the other side of my cheek and continued, "Don't answer to the words of your uncle that you will be nothing or that you are ugly, don't let the pain of your parents letting you down hold you down any more."

He continued "If we expect nothing out of life, life will give us nothing. But, if we expect great things from ourselves and great things out of life, then we will strive towards being the best we can be."

I did not know what to say, no one had ever spoken to me like this before. No one had ever told me that I could really be someone.

"When you look at me, what do you see?" I asked Eddie.

"I see someone who has been hurt, someone who is angry, someone who expects little out of life, but demands much. But, I also see someone who if she let her real light shine, would light up not only her life, but the lives of all the people around her."

Belief & Expectations

"Do you really believe that of me?" I asked.

"Yes," said Eddie. Then, he sat down beside me and said, "Emma, I do believe in you. However, you must also believe in yourself.

You must expect good things from yourself and life. In fact you must expect more from yourself than anyone else expects from you."

I realised at that moment that I had been living my life through other people's expectations and limitations and that I had to now take responsibility and control of my life.

"I am beautiful," I said to myself realising that I had to raise my expectations of myself. "I will be somebody," I told myself. "I will not live by anybody else's limitations, I will not be afraid to shine."

Eddie smiled as he heard these words, stood up, kissed me on the cheek and went back inside. He knew that a transformation had begun, that a new Emma was being born, one with high expectations of herself and her life.

Did the spoilt Emma go away? Don't be silly! I actually enjoyed being a little spoilt, so I kept her around for a while longer, although she only came out on rare occasions.

The new Emma was wonderful. I had never felt so positive and full of life. I now knew and believed I could be someone if I really tried. It was a wonderful feeling that made me feel really great about myself.

It was some time after whilst playing a truth or dare game with the other members of 'The RESPECT crew' that I was asked whether I wanted a 'dare or to tell the truth' by Colin.

I do not know why he asked me this question, but he did, and the question was, "Have you ever run away from home?" That was easy for me and I said, "Yes" and then quickly added that I had also slept on the street for one night.

Colin looked shocked, spoilt little Emma had run away from home and slept on the streets! He could not believe it. "You're lying," he said, "You have never run away from home. You have always had a home, you do not even know what it is like to not have a real family," he said.

"Really?" I said "Then tell me what it's like?" I asked

"OK then, I will" he said.

This is Colin's story.

The Sixth Principle

There are consequences for every choice we make in life. Some are good and some are bad, a fact we cannot hide from. So make choices that will have good outcomes.

CONSEQUENCES

My name is Colin, this is my story.

𝕴 **have always wondered whether I was like my dad.** I do not know and doubt whether I will ever know because I never knew him. In fact, I never knew my mum either.

I was told I was a product of two people who did not even really know each other.

They got drunk one night and conceived me. The man did not even know my mum was pregnant and as soon as I was born, my mother put me in a home. She told the staff her story, left and never came back for me.

The Home

I was a mistake, conceived by two people who did not care at all about how I was going to survive. One of my first memories as a child was being beaten up by some other kids in the home I was in.

It was a home for abandoned kids. I was a skinny kid, a wimpish pale boy who looked like I could do with a blood transfusion.

I had nobody who really cared for me, so from an early age I had to care for myself. I was one of the youngest in the home and I used to get bullied all the time.

I remember one winter's night when the other boys decided to have a laugh and they took all my clothes off and threw me outside in the snow and locked the door.

I remember being so cold I went blue. I could not stop shivering. When they let me back in the boys gave me a beating just for the fun of it. Did I complain? Oh no, it was a way of life for me, I knew no better. If I did complain I knew I would get it worse next time. Anyway, no one cared what happen to Colin.

My First Home

I was about seven when I went to the first of many family homes. These were homes that would keep me for a while. At last, a real home I thought.

How mistaken I was because it was horrible. Even though I was only seven, for the next two years they treated me like a servant. I had so many chores to do before and after school that I used to fall asleep in class.

The teachers thought I was not paying attention, so from an early age I started getting a reputation and was always in trouble in school. After a while, I just could not be bothered anymore and started acting exactly how the teachers said I was acting. I was a terror in school.

Home, if you could call it that, was a place that meant work and more work. My foster parents owned a restaurant and I was the skivvy at the back.

They used to have a cane that they would smack me with if I did not do as they asked.

I remember the cane so well, it used to make a swoosh sound as it went through the air on its way to my legs, back or arms.

It seemed they cared more for the potatoes I used to peel than for me. After a two year period with this family, I went to a nicer family on the other side of town.

They were a very nice elderly couple. For the first time I was treated with a little love. They were really nice to me. It only lasted for a short while, as his wife died of natural causes and the husband decided that he could not cope with me by himself so I was shipped off to another family.

This family had two daughters already and they wanted a son, but could not have any more children so they decided to take me in for a while.

I do not want to sound ungrateful, but their two daughters made the ugly sisters in the Cinderella story look good. They were just as mean.

If any one of them was Sleeping Beauty and they required a kiss from me to wake up… they would have slept forever. 'Tweedledum' and 'Tweedledee' I used to call them. We would argue all the time and their mum and dad were never on my side even when they knew I was in the right.

Revenge Is Sweet

We had a cat that I had to look after. His name was 'George' and he was an old, fat cat who could catch a mouse if he tried. I remember one day I had to help cook.

The sisters upset me real badly that day, so I chopped up some cat food and put it in their favorite dish, mince meat and onions. I laughed as I watched them eat up every last drop.

Did I care if they had found out? No, I did not, I just wanted to get them back for being mean to me.

After two years of arguing with the ugly sisters, I left to go to another home. By this time I had been in a home for seven years with no love and care and two family homes with no love and care.

How was I supposed to care about anyone when I had never been shown care by anyone?

I felt that if nobody cared about me then I would not care about anyone, and I started a lifestyle of doing all sorts of bad things to property and people and did not care if I got caught.

A Turnaround

As I got older I went through a growth spurt and found myself getting bigger and stronger. The little pale skin wimpish boy started turning into a tall, strong boy who could intimidate other boys with his size.

I could not believe the turnaround for me. The boy who was once bullied and beaten could now be the bully and start beating other boys and get away with it.

I set myself on a journey to get a reputation as a bad boy who could fight and would hurt you if you crossed his path.

To be honest with you, I knew bullying was wrong, but still found it fun. I did not like the fighting though. I knew every time I got into a fight that I was really risking my life.

There were so many boys around my age that were being killed over stupidness, it was silly. They were dying by accident or on purpose, but they were still dying or getting a serious injury.

I just felt I had to fight, I felt it was the only way to get respect on the streets, and since that's where I spent most of my time, I had to gain respect.

The Prankster

At school, I did not get on with most of my teachers. My head of year was always giving me detention. I used to call him 'Forest Gump' as he looked like the actor in the film.

I was kind of a practical joker at school and I decided to play a trick on him. He had his own office with a black phone in it. I waited for the day his office was unlocked, and I crept in and took out some shoe polish I had in my pocket.

I coated the receiver of the phone in his office with the polish and then put it back on the receiver.

I waited for him to walk by his office and I rang his office number. He ran in and picked up the phone. I starting laughing down the phone.

I was just around the corner so he could not hear me. I then walked past his office and smiled as he was busy wiping the shoe polish off his hands, it was so funny.

Did I care if he found out it was me? No, not really.

A prank that I did get in trouble for is one I pulled on my history teacher. She was so boring she even made the head nerd of the school fall asleep.

During lunch one day, I sneaked into her classroom. She had one of those old desks that used to have an open lid, which she used to lift up and put her things in. When she was out of the class I lifted the lid and put loads of super glue around the edges and pressed the lid down tightly so that it would stick together.

We had history the next lesson and I watched as she struggled to open her desk. She was going red. It was after about five minutes of her trying before she realised what had happened. She looked straight at me, and I could not help it, I just burst out laughing.

I did think it was unfair to get a five day exclusion just for that. Come on, people sometimes only get three days for fighting! It just confirmed my thoughts that the school did not like me.

A Small Act

The next day, what I would have said was a small incident happened, which was to have such very sad consequences. I could never have known.

It started when I took a PS2 Game Boy from a small boy. I just saw him using it and told him to give it to me. I told him if he told anyone I would beat him up. He tried to stop me, so I slapped him round the head to shake him up a bit. Eventually, he gave me the Game Boy.

I thought nothing of it. It was something I had done before and had no comebacks, but this time was going to be different. The boy I had taken the Game Boy from happened to be the little brother of a guy that had left our school two years earlier.

I forgot all about it. It was about a year later when I was walking down the high street near my school when I saw the boy whom I had taken the Game Boy from. I did not remember him at first. It was only when he gave me an intense look that the memory came back.

He had remembered me immediately. Why should he forget me anyway, he had only one face to remember, mine. I had too many faces to remember of the people I had done something to. The boy was not alone as he had two older boys with him. As he saw me, he shouted out "There he is!"

The Chase

The two boys left his side and ran straight for me. I stood strong, looked straight at them and then did what every strong, proud boy or man in that position would have done… I ran for my life.

Now, I was never into athletics, but on this day I was a hundred-meter champion. I ran straight for some flats I knew and ran round by where the bins were.

These boys were fast and they were right behind me. I was getting out of breath, so I decided to hide in the one place I did not think they would find me, the large plastic bins. I lifted the lid of one of them, jumped in and stayed quiet.

All I remember was the smell of rotten fish and milk and it was awful. I began to wonder what was worse: the smell or them beating me up. I went for the smell and stayed there for what must have been an hour.

While I was in the bin I started thinking about what I had done to the boy. It was the first time I had ever attempted to consider the consequences of my actions, but I dismissed it quickly. I did not want to face up to things.

After about half an hour, I saw the lid of the bin being lifted off. "Shit! They found me," I thought and was preparing myself for a beating only to feel a black plastic bag hit my head as somebody emptied their rubbish into the bin.

I thought, that's it... whether they are out there or not, I am getting out now. I stood up to see if the coast was clear. There was nobody around so I quickly made my way home.

Crushed Grapes

On the way home I was laughing to myself about being in the bin and having rubbish dropped on me when I felt someone grab me and pull me to the floor. I looked up it was the two boys who had chased me earlier. They had waited for me where I lived.

Then it started, it was like they were crushing grapes with their hands and feet as they laid into me for what seemed like ages. As they beat me they said, "This is what you get for stealing our little brother's Game Boy."

They only stopped when someone came out of their house and

said they were going to call the police. As they ran off they said that they had not finished with me yet and that they would be back for more.

I picked myself up and stumbled home bruised from the attack and smelly from the bins. Did I believe I got what I deserved? No I did not, and I just swore I would get my revenge.

The Knife

My step dad had a hunting knife he always kept in the cupboard under the stairs. I went to look for it as I decided that from that day I was going to carry a knife for protection and that I would never get beaten up like that again.

I knew the consequences of carrying a knife, the jail term, a criminal record, someone getting hurt or killed, even myself getting hurt, but I just brushed them off.

When I first left the house with the knife in my pocket, to be honest I knew it was a stupid thing to do, but I still did it. It somehow gave me more confidence. Again, I knew this was a false confidence.

I kept asking myself if I would use it if I had to. I started to make up all the reasons I could for carrying the knife and all the reasons I could for having to use it…for protection only of course.

The Visit

I felt humiliated by the beating I had received and wanted to get my own back. I had an idea where the brothers who beat me up hung out and decided I was going to pay them a visit with my new metal friend.

I only wanted to shake them up a bit, but could never have imagined what was about to happen. If I did, I would never have gone to look for them.

I felt I could not go alone and so I went to knock for Dane and Tim, two guys I knew who could fight and defend themselves. What I

THE SIXTH PRINCIPLE - CONSEQUENCES

did not do was tell them what had happened or what we were going to do. I just told them to come and jam with me for the day.

We went to area where I thought the boys might be hanging about and looked around for while. We asked one or two people, but as we did not see them we went home.

My two friends were still unsuspecting at this time.

How the brothers got to find out that we were looking for them, I do not know. But, they did and they came looking for us.

It was the following day. By this point, I had decided that I was going to forget about it when word got back to me that the brothers were coming for me.

I quickly went to call on Dane and Tim, again not telling them what was going on. I just thought that if the brothers saw me with Dane and Tim, they would just leave it and not bother to step up to me.

How wrong I was! What I did not know at the time was that these two brothers had a reputation in their ends, and the fact that I had come to their ends to look for them was a sign of disrespect that they could not let go.

We were sitting on the wall of my flats when across the road appeared the brothers, only there were three other people with them. When I saw them I shouted out, "Oh my God!"

Tim said, "What's wrong, Colin?" Before I could answer him the five of them were rushing at us from across the road.

The Fight

Dane shouted out "What's this about, Colin, are they coming for you?" Before I could answer him they were in our faces.

Dane did not like anyone being up in his face, so even though he did not know what was going on, he was mad and pushed one of the boys back. Then it started, all hell broke loose as the five of them steamed into us.

The Hope Dealer - Always consider the consequences of your actions.   87

Dane and Tim could really fight, but as there were five of them they were getting the better of us. Two of them jumped on Tim, got him on the floor and started to punch and kick him.

I could see he was getting hurt, so I pulled out my step dad's hunting knife and held it up for the boys to see.

They stopped for a moment and looked at the knife glimmering in the sun. I thought that would have been the end of it, but one of the boys picked up a plank of wood, which was on the floor and came straight for me.

He took a swing at me so what was I supposed to do? I leaned to one side and just found myself thrusting the knife towards him, aiming at his body. My eyes were closed by this time and I was thrusting with all my might.

Then there was an almighty scream… not from the boy who I had tried to stab, but from me as he had somehow managed to whack my arm with the plank of wood. The blade fell out of my hand. One of the brothers leant forward and picked it up.

The blade was now in their possession. I remember saying in my mind, "This does not look good!" The brother moved towards me holding the knife out as he came towards my body. I was in pain from my arm being hit with the plank of wood. I could not defend myself properly.

A Fatal Mistake

I am going to get stabbed, I thought. Shit! I am going to get stabbed. As the brother lunged forward with the knife, Dane who had been next to me tried to grab the knife from the boy. It turned out be a foolish and fatal mistake.

As he tried to grab the knife, the boy turned and the momentum of Dane coming forward and the brother turning made the incident unstoppable. The knife went into Dane's side, and he let out and almighty scream.

"They've stabbed Dane!" I screamed, "They've stabbed Dane!" The brother, realising what he had done dropped the knife, turned and ran. His brother and other mates followed him.

What a disaster! How could this have happened, I thought? I knelt down and spoke to Dane who was now in a pool of blood.

"It's going to be OK" I said, "It's going to be OK. I am so sorry for getting you involved in this, I am so sorry!" Dane was looking pale and was gasping for air. Tim was on his mobile phone screaming for an ambulance.

"My friend has been stabbed!" he shouted. "My friend has been stabbed, come now, please hurry!"

Dane started to spit out blood.

"Oh God!" I thought. "He is going to die and it's my fault." I held his head up in a desperate attempt to stop him from choking on his blood. I sat there for five minutes waiting for the ambulance to come, watching Dane's body go into spasms.

I could hear the sirens of the ambulance. "Hurry up," I thought, "he is going to die."

The ambulance screeched to a halt and the ambulance men raced out of the van and over to Dane. I stepped back as they frantically tried to save him.

"How is he?" I shouted as I could not see what they were doing. There was no answer from the team. "How is he?" I said again, in a panic. There was a pause, then one of the crew turned around and just shook his head.

Reflection Time

For a brief moment, time seemed to stand still. I traced back the things that led to this incident. Me stealing the Game Boy from the boy, then me being chased by the brothers, me hiding in the bin, then them beating me up.

Then me getting my step dad's hunting knife, me calling for Tim and Dane to go look for them, then the big fight. Me pulling out the knife, the knife dropping, the look in the boy's eyes as he picked up the knife, Dane moving to help me and then the sound of Dane screaming as he was stabbed.

Now, my friend was lying there... dead!

I sank my head into my hands and cried like a baby. When I think back, the tears were partly for my friend, but also for me. How could I have been so stupid, look what I had caused!

What made me cry even more was the fact that it was my knife that was used to stab my friend. Something I should not have been carrying in the first place.

All this happened because I stole a Game Boy, which I sold for only £30. Was it worth it? I said to myself. *Was my friend's life worth it?* The memory of that day still haunts me and will haunt me for the rest of my life.

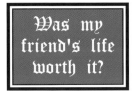

They caught the guy that stabbed Dane, but that did not matter... my friend was dead, all because of me.

I had spent my whole life not caring what happened to me, not caring whether I got caught and not caring who knew about what I was doing.

I could never have dreamed that a small incident that happened so long ago could come back to haunt me in such a big way. My friend was with me that day because I was protecting myself. I did not really care about him.

He died trying to save me after I had done something stupid. He was killed by my knife, which I should not have been carrying anyway.

A Lesson Not Learnt

The time had come for me to accept that there are consequences to the choices I make and the things I do, and to also realise that sometimes people around me can also be affected by the consequences of my actions.

I am going to be a changed young man. I am no longer going to take so many stupid risks, not caring about what happens or whether I get caught. I am going to mature, be responsible and think more before I do something.

That's what should have happened, but did I learn? No, I never did. I could have been telling you this story from my prison cell. I got caught carrying a knife and a gun after an attempted robbery. I have just finished my sentence.

There are names for young men like me and the nicest of them is "damn stupid." I heard an old woman say once "those who cannot hear will feel."

I did not listen and had felt the loneliness of a prison cell for a few years. I did not listen to the voices in my head or my life experiences that were telling me to change my attitude and life style.

It occurred to me that for so long I had played the prankster, not caring who got hurt as long as I had a laugh, but I certainly am not laughing now.

The only positive thing was that when I started my sentence, my step dad told me that it was such a waste being in prison for five years.

He said that people could get degrees in three. I listened to that comment, and I caught up on some of the education I missed when I messed about in school.

It was not the same though, all my friends would have been to college and some more than likely have gotten a good job already.

I am not going to complain. I had my chances, I did not care and I messed up too many times.

I missed the crew while inside. They all came to see me now and again. The person that visited me the most was Tracey. Even though she knew I was in the wrong, she did not lay into me like my parents and the rest of the crew did.

She would always be the first person to arrive at the prison. She was never late and prided herself on being on time.

It was like she was obsessed by time and how she used it. I know she was not always like this. She used to be terrible.

This is Tracey's story.

The Seventh Principle

If you do not respect time, time will not respect you.
Tomorrow belongs to the people that invest time in
themselves and others today.

TIME

My name is Tracey, this is my story.

𝕴 **used to always hear my mum say**, "Girl, the older you get the quicker time will go by." She would say to me that if I did not respect time, time would not respect me and before I knew it I would have none left.

I did not appreciate what she meant back then, but now I do. I learnt the hard way. I learnt how important it was to respect time, be on time and to use time wisely.

I thought nothing of my mum's comments. I was young and care free and as far I was concerned, whatever I missed out on now, I could catch up with at a later date. I was to learn that there are times when you only get one shot, and if it is wasted, you may never get a chance to get it back.

What I was not always fully aware of was how my lack of respect for time and bad time keeping used to really upset my friends. I always took it for a joke when I was late, but they, I was to find out, did not.

Friendships and Time

I remember this one particular time, when because I was late, it affected one of my long term friendships. I had a really good friend called Sharon and we used to do a lot of things together.

Sharon was one of my best friends. She recently met this really nice boy and because I had really pestered her, she set up a date for me with one of his friends.

His name was Steve, and she could not stop talking about him. He was so good-looking with nice manners. She was really excited about the fact that she thought the boy was so good-looking.

He could get so many others girls, however, he had shown an interest in her.

There was a new film out that Sharon and Steve wanted to see. She knew it would be a popular screening, so Sharon asked Steve to book some tickets in advance so we would not have to queue when we got there. We would also be guaranteed entry.

Sharon had arranged to meet with Steve and his friend at 7.15pm outside the cinema. She arranged to meet me thirty minutes earlier in the Pizza Hut nearby.

We were really excited. We even decided that we were going to arrive five minutes late just so we didn't look too keen. I had a lot to do that day and was rushing around as usual trying to get as many things done as possible.

I remember getting a phone call from Sharon about 5pm telling me not to be late. She knew my time keeping was bad. I told her not to worry, that this time I was going to be on time.

"If you are late," she said. "I will never speak to you again." Sharon had said this many times before, so I just brushed it off... little did I realise how this time was going to be different.

If you are late," she said. "I will never speak to you again

Lost in Time

The time just went so quickly and I did not mean to do it. I just got so caught up that by the time I looked at my watch again, it was 6.30pm and I was not even ready.

I remember I was traveling home on the bus, which got stuck in traffic. I jumped off the bus and ran all the way home since it was only a few stops away. I rushed into the house and up to my room to decide what I was going to wear.

This was never a quick decision for me, and I just could not decide what look to go for. As I did not even have time to phone Sharon to see what she was wearing, it was even more difficult. Finally, I just grabbed a pair of jeans and a top and put them out on the bed to wear.

I looked at the time. Oh no! I still need to have a shower, I thought. I had been out all day. No time for a shower, I thought, so I did the next best thing I could thing of.

I just put some soap and water on a flannel and had a quick 'wipe and go' under my arms and anywhere else I had time to do. A girl has to do these things when she is in a rush.

Just an extra bit of perfume will do the trick.

Late Again

Before I knew it the time was 7.45pm and I had not even met Sharon yet. She is going to kill me, I thought, as I rushed down to the Pizza Hut to meet her. By the time I got to her it was 8pm.

When she saw me coming she was mad as a hatter.

"How could you do this?" she said. "You know how much this evening means to me, you just think of yourself! You're so selfish and disrespectful. If you mess up me and Steve I will hate you for ever. I could not even call him to say that we were going to be late as I have no credit on my phone."

I always had an excuse for why I was late, but on this occasion I had none. I knew I had messed up. I had never seen Sharon like this. I had been late so many times before, but this time was different.

She had never called me selfish of disrespectful. I had never even thought about my being late in that way.

Was I being selfish and disrespectful by being late all the time? I had no time to think about it at that moment, as I was so scared that Steve would not be there. We were now one hour late for meeting him and his friends.

The Text

As we approached the cinema, Sharon got a text that stopped her in her tracks. When she read the text she just looked up at me and said, "I will never forgive you!" I grabbed the phone from her hands and read the text.

It said "Shaz, I ave been waiting 45minz nw, u have not even foned me, thats disrespectful, I spent my money on u. Met 2 friends from skool n ave given them ur tkts film is gr8 n we r avin a gd tym, don't call me, I will call you. L8rs."

The Truth Hurts

My mouth dropped. How could he be so cheeky?
I shouted out, "He could have waited for us!"
"That's your problem," Sharon shouted back.
"You think everyone should wait for you and you think nothing about messing up other people's plans because of your bad time keeping.

I had met a really nice boy and tried to help you by setting you up with his friend and this is how you repay me, by messing up my chances."

I was stunned and did not know what to say. I just held my head down in shame.

Sharon just walked off and left me there to think about how I had really messed up this time. Sharon did not speak to me for nearly a year after that incident and even when she did, it was never the same.

It was not that she had made a boy come between us. It was the fact that I was always late and inconsiderate and I did not think about how my timekeeping affected other people.

It was a harsh lesson, but I did I learn to respect time more… no, not yet. It took another incident, something that scared me so much I decided that I would have to change my ways.

The incident with Sharon really upset me, however, in my mind I thought she was taking it too far by not talking to me. So, I just spent more time with two of my other friends Jill and Rita.

The Party Girls

I had known Jill and Rita for a while now since they both went to the same primary school as me. We lost touch, but we all met up again one night at another friend's birthday party.

Jill and Rita loved to go out. They were what you might call 'good time girls' who always knew how to be the life and soul of the party. If you ever need someone to get a party started, then Jill and Rita would be the best people to have around.

You would never have known it from the way they behaved at times, but they were A star students. They just knew when to put their heads down to work, and when to party and have a good time.

The Birthday Event

It was Jill's birthday and she decided that she was going to the West End to celebrate her birthday. She decided that she did not want a big group as we were all under the age of sixteen and too many girls would attract the wrong attention.

So only four of us were in the group, and we all met at Rita's house to get ready. As we were leaving Rita's house, I looked at the four of us.

We all looked older than our ages, so I knew that we would be able to get into the club we were going to. In my mind, I felt sorry for any boy that might cross our path tonight. We were out for some serious girl fun.

I actually arrived on time at Rita's house for once, but that was where my good timekeeping stopped that evening. We were all excited when we left Rita's house, jumped on the bus and headed for the West End.

We got to the club nice and early and had no trouble, as I suspected, in getting in. We were having such a good time in the club and Jill was having a great birthday.

It was about 12.30am and the club was open until 3.00am. But, because we had spent our cab fare money, we all decided that we would take the night bus home. It was due to come at 1.00am, and anyway, it would drop us right outside our homes.

We agreed to spend fifteen more minutes in the club and all meet in reception where we had left our coats. We all rushed back in for our last dance.

There was a cute boy who had been looking at me all night. As I went back in, he asked me to dance. I thought, great, just as I am getting ready to leave, this cute boy asks me for a dance.

Dance Fever

Did I say no? Of course not, and with a big grin we headed for the dance floor. The DJ was really good and was dropping some really hot tunes.

I was right in the flow when I felt someone grab me by the scruff of my neck.

It was Jill. "Don't you know what time it is?"

"No," I said, straightening my clothes and smiling at the boy, trying to hide my embarrassment.

"It's 1.05am and we all agreed to meet in the reception over 20 minutes ago. We have all been waiting for you while you were strutting your stuff on the dance floor."

"Sorry, I just got caught up and forgot about the time," I replied.

Jill just grabbed my arm and we headed for the door. I did not even have time to say goodbye properly to the boy I had met.

We all rushed out of the club down to the bus stop. As we got round the corner, we could see our bus waiting at the bus stop.

We started to run even faster, shouting out to the driver to wait for us. But, he did not hear us and we watched in horror as the last bus moved off without us on board.

Stranded

"What are we going to do now?" said Christine one of the girls in the group. "I promised my dad I would be home before a certain time.

He is going to kill me if I do not get home."

"I am sorry I made us miss the bus," I said "I am really sorry."

"I am dead!" shouted out Christine and she started to cry.

I said, "Look don't cry, you will get home in time.

"How?" she asked.

"Look we can take a cab," I said.

"No we can't!" said Rita. "We've spent our cab money!"

"I will pay for the cab," I told them.

They all looked at me a little stunned.

"You will pay for it?" Rita asked.

"Yes, I will pay. I have some money at home and because I was the one that made us late, I will pay for the cab home."

I did not have to repeat myself. Before I had taken a breath, Christine had flagged down a cab and was getting in it.

"Come on!" she shouted and we all got in.

The Cab Drive

The ride home was quiet and I did not say a word. Mainly because I was thinking in my mind, "How am I going to pay for this cab?" When I got home, I did not have any money to pay for the cab! I just said it to look good.

I was hoping they would have just said they would wait for the next bus, but they did not. Now, we were all in a cab, which I would have to pay for in some way.

The cab dropped Christine off first, then Jill. There was only myself and Rita left in the cab. I knew at that point what I was going to have to do.

I told Rita I was taking her home first, even though I would have had to come back on myself to go home.

As Rita got out of the cab and waved goodbye, I looked at the meter and thought, "There is no way I am going to pay for this, so there is only one thing left for me to do."

I had heard my cousin talking of a time when she had done it. It was wrong and she should not have, but it was the only thing she could do as there was a time when she did not have any money to pay the cab man either.

I saw the cab man was looking at me and smiling so I decided to make my move. I said "Look, sir, I know this is going to sound a bit funny, but I might not have enough money to pay you for the cab. But, I might be able to pay you in another way."

I was so scared. I was at least a two miles from home in a cab with no money to pay for it, about to do something I had never done before in my life.

By this time, the driver must have had all sorts of thoughts going through his mind as he brought the car to a stop on a quiet road.

As the car stopped I said, "Let me get out and come round to the front seat." As I opened the door, I thought, "What am I doing, this is just because I had no respect for time."

As I opened the door I look at the driver and shouted out "Sorry!" and I grabbed my bag and ran as fast as I could in the other direction.

Alone and Scared

My heart was beating so fast, I did not even look back. I do not even know if he chased me. All I know was that I was out of one dilemma into another. I was around a mile from home, it was late, dark and I was really scared.

I knew what direction I had to walk in so I started to walk. After about five minutes a car passed me, went up the road around 200 yards, and turned round and headed towards me.

Now I was really scared. I turned down an alleyway and the car followed me. Oh my God, I thought, I am going to be attacked. I started to run.

My heart was beating so fast, as I started running. All I remember saying to myself was, "Please! Please God, let me be safe. I will never be late for anything again never... never!"

The car pulled up beside me and I heard someone shout out "Tracey!" They know my name, I thought.

"It's me, Tracey... Steve". I was so scared so it did not register, and I just kept on running.

Then, I realised who was in the car. Steve was my next door neighbour's oldest son. He had been out for the night and was on his way home when he saw me walking by myself and decided to offer me a lift home.

This was a boy, who I had not really got on with or spoken much to, but at that moment it was so good to see him. I jumped into the back seat of his car and we headed towards my house.

Reflection Time

As we drove home I reflected on how my lack of respect for time had affected my life and the lives of other people around me. My lateness had affected my school work as I was always late for school and my classes.

It had damaged my friendship with Sharon, a girl whom I really liked and got on with.

With my heart still beating fast, I thought about how it had caused me to have to break the law and do a runner from a cab. Then, it caused me to be scared out of my life with the thought of being attacked.

The time had come for me to respect time more, and I swore that from that moment on, I would do all I could to make sure that I was not only on time, but that I would leave enough time so that I did not have to rush.

It took a long time for me to learn, but learn I did, and everyone noticed the difference in me. I even noticed the difference in myself, as I was a lot calmer in my actions, and was not rushing around whenever I had to do something because I left more than enough time to do what I had to do.

RESPECTisms

the word on the street

The Wrap Up

Speaking of time, it's been a while since the RESPECT crew met up lately. We have all been busy getting on with our own lives. I have to say that I am really glad we all met up that day in the park that day and stayed friends because we have helped each other in so many ways.

Robert

We are all meeting up later on today. You remember Sarah? It's her son's fourth birthday party and we will all be there. I thought she would have chosen Eddie, but she chose Robert to be her son's Godfather.

I must admit he has been great and has been really responsible, taking the role seriously and helping Sarah out where he can. Boy, has he changed over the years, time has certainly matured him.

Eddie

Eddie will be there, of course. The only question will be what young lady will he be with? It is amazing how he used to be teased in school by the girls and now they can't get enough of him... education definitely pays.

He has so many choices he can make about his future. One thing is for sure, with his education he will never be poor.

Sarah

Sarah is OK. She has made a great mum. She always speaks of her regret at what happened. Not about having the baby, but what happened to make her have the baby.

Her life has gone completely in a different direction to what she wanted. As she always reminds us, it was all because she did not say no when she should have. I really learnt from her mistake.

Peter

Peter will definitely be there. Where two or three people are gathered, Peter will appear. He loves a group atmosphere and would never miss a party. He is not as bad as he used to be.

He still can't stand to be by himself, but he is far more careful and less trusting of the people he starts to get to know. He is like a preacher with us and everyone he gets to know, preaching the gospel of 'Beware of the Frienemys'.

Emma

Emma is still her spoilt self at times, though not as bad. I am sure she likes being that way because she gets people's attention at least. Who would have thought that she had such low self-esteem and expected so little of herself. That's not the case now.

With Eddie as her motivational coach, she really believes in herself and now expects so much out of life. It is always good to see her though.

Colin

Colin may never learn his lesson. He is lucky he is out in time to be there. I hated visiting him in prison, but somehow just found myself being there for him in a non-judgmental way.

If there was one of the crew that needed a good kick up the backside, it was Colin. Even though he is out now, I still don't believe that he gets it, no matter what he says. I hope his last experience has shown him the consequences that his actions can bring... only time will tell.

Respect

As you can see 'time' and 'respect' has played an important part in all our lives as we have all grown up learning from each other. Well, at least some of us have.

Being part of the 'RESPECT Crew' has made such a major impact on our lives. In fact, the word 'respect' is something we all will have in the forefront of our minds for the rest of our lives.

The word respect and the 'isims' and 'schisms' of our life stories, called RESPECTisms will play a big part in the rest of our lives.
Just noticed the time. I am not late, but want to leave enough time to get ready and not rush.

I said I would be at Sarah's baby's party early, so I must go now. Before I leave though, I want to leave you with a message from myself and the rest of the 'RESPECT Crew'.

Memorise this message and repeat it all the time to yourself, even put it up on your bedroom wall. It will inspire you to do the right things in life.

The Final Message

Always remember to take Responsibility for your own actions, that Education gives you choices... education is the key to success.

Say No to negative influences and people.

Know your Peers, for their influence can affect your growth and development.

Expect more from yourself than others expect from you.

For every choice you make in life, remember there are always Consequences, some good and some bad.

And, finally, Time waits for no one, so don't waste it. Tomorrow belongs to the young people who prepare for it today.

About The Author

Ken **Barnes is the principal consultant of c-a-n-i**, a multi-disciplined agency that focuses on personal and professional growth and development. "Yesterday's knowledge is today's ignorance" is one of Ken's most used statements, and as such, he passionately believes that learning is a continuous and never-ending process.

Ken is a government advisor on raising the aspirations and attainment of young people. He has numerous other titles such as entrepreneur, author, motivational speaker, coach and community business leader. However, the title that gives Ken the most personal satisfaction is the title of mentor. Through his professional and personal life activities, Ken has inspired thousands of adults and children to reflect and to discover the valuable personal assets they posses within themselves.

Ken has been honoured with a number of awards for his work which include; Men of Merit, Man of Valour and The City of London

ABOUT THE AUTHOR

Police.   His powerful method for change 'Transition through Introspection' empowers individuals to self reflect, recognise and analyse their core strengths and competencies.

His methodology has been inspired by over eighteen years in the field of training and development.

His passionate style of delivery, in-depth subject knowledge infused with humour is sure to inspire, motivate and challenge you.

His commitment to delivering inspirational messages will always leave you empowered, focused and ready for the next exciting challenge that life offers you.

Ken cares about his community and invests his time and resources in a number of good causes.

He is either the leader or on the board of a number of charitable and community initiatives internationally, nationally and on a more local basis.